2015 AOTA
Salary & Workforce
Survey

AOTA
PRESS
The American
Occupational Therapy
Association, Inc.

AOTA® The American
Occupational Therapy
Association, Inc.

AOTA Centennial Vision

We envision that occupational therapy is a powerful, widely recognized, science-driven, and evidence-based profession with a globally connected and diverse workforce meeting society's occupational needs.

Mission Statement

The American Occupational Therapy Association advances the quality, availability, use, and support of occupational therapy through standard-setting, advocacy, education, and research on behalf of its members and the public.

AOTA Staff

Frederick P. Somers, *Executive Director*
Christopher M. Bluhm, *Chief Operating Officer*
Melissa Stutzbach, *Project Coordinator*

Chris Davis, *Director, AOTA Press*
Caroline Polk, *Digital Manager and* AJOT *Managing Editor*
Ashley Hofmann, *Development Editor*
Barbara Dickson, *Production Editor*
Joe King-Shaw, *AOTA Press Business and Customer Service Administrator*

Rebecca Rutberg, *Director, Marketing*
Amanda Goldman, *Marketing Manager*
Jennifer Folden, *Marketing, Graphic Designer*

American Occupational Therapy Association, Inc.
4720 Montgomery Lane
Bethesda, MD 20814
Phone: 301-652-AOTA (2682)
TDD: 800-377-8555
Fax: 301-652-7711
www.aota.org

To order: 1-877-404-AOTA or store.aota.org

Disclaimers

This publication is designed to provide accurate and authoritative information in regard to the subject matter covered. It is sold or distributed with the understanding that the publisher is not engaged in rendering legal, accounting, or other professional service. If legal advice or other expert assistance is required, the services of a competent professional person should be sought.
—*From the Declaration of Principles jointly adopted by the American Bar Association and a Committee of Publishers and Associations*

It is the objective of the American Occupational Therapy Association to be a forum for free expression and interchange of ideas. The opinions expressed by the contributors to this work are their own and not necessarily those of the American Occupational Therapy Association.

ISBN-13: 978-1-56900-376-3
Library of Congress Control Number: 2015944617

Cover Design by Jennifer Folden
Composition by Jennifer Folden
Printed by Automated Graphic Systems, Inc., White Plains, MD

Contents

Purpose of and Using This Report

As the professional association serving occupational therapy, AOTA regularly monitors and measures workforce and compensation trends. The survey includes demographic information as well as detailing where occupational therapy practitioners are working, how they are compensated, and what benefits they commonly receive. The report also investigates student attitudes toward the vitality of the job market and the profession overall.

This report is segmented into modules, with each centering on a specific focal point of the research. Although it is helpful to explore the full report, each module was designed to be a stand-alone unit and can be read independently of the other modules without substantial loss of detail.

The report begins with the Project Overview, which explores the research approach, methodology, and other overview topics. It should be read before any of the modules to put all data in proper context. A brief synopsis of the focus of each module follows.

Module 1: Profile of the Profession

Module 1 concentrates on baseline demographics of the profession, exploring metrics such as age, gender, educational background, and occupational therapist (OT) and occupational therapy assistant (OTA) status. The goal is to provide a statistical snapshot of occupational therapy practitioners and highlight trends in comparison with past *American Occupational Therapy Association (AOTA) Salary and Workforce Survey* samples. Although this type of information lacks significant probative value (other than interesting statistical "tidbits" on the profession), it is an essential component of the *AOTA Salary and Workforce Survey* because it defines the sample parameters on which all other data are based.

Module 2: Work Setting Overview and Profile

Module 2 continues to build a profile of the profession, but the data are centered on work setting issues. In addition to exploring where the respondents work, this module explores some key workforce issues such as

- Organizational and ownership status of respondents' employers

- Prevalence of self-employment in the profession
- Prevalence of working in multiple settings (more detailed information on specific settings is provided in Modules 7–16).

Module 3: Compensation Overview

Module 3 covers the core focus of the survey—how much do those in the occupational therapy profession earn, and how has this income changed over the past several years? Compensation data are explored in two basic formats. First, this module provides overview data, characterizing respondents by overarching metrics such as their work classification (e.g., part-time vs. full-time), years of experience, location, work setting, and others. Each metric is examined independently for OTs and OTAs. These data are intended to provide a broad overview of compensation practices in the profession and explore how compensation is affected by key metrics. Second, more detailed data are provided in Modules 7–16, which explore compensation (among other factors) for each individual work setting. Within each setting, the data are broken out by multiple metrics. Both the overview data in this module and the detailed data in Modules 7–16 explore different, but equally important, facets of the compensation landscape.

Module 4: Benefits

Module 4 explores baseline benefits received by the respondents and whether the benefits are received at their primary work setting, their secondary (or other) work setting, or both. Only basic benefits are examined, such as health insurance, state licensure fees, pension plans, and similar benefits that are typically considered standard in many work environments. To keep the survey length manageable, details such as the amount the employer pays for employees' health insurance premiums and the number of days received as paid time off were not collected. The respondents were asked to indicate only which benefits they receive and if they were through their primary or secondary (or other) work setting (or both).

Module 5: Workforce Dynamics

Module 5 explores a variety of issues related to the dynamics affecting the occupational therapy workforce. These issues include job mobility (e.g., how often practitioners change jobs), reasons for job changes, unemployment rates in the profession for 2014, and the perceptions of those who are looking to leave the profession.

Module 6: Students

Module 6 is limited to the 1,273 people who identified themselves as either a full-time or part-time student in the occupational therapy field and were not employed in the occupational therapy profession in 2014. These people were not asked the in-depth questions concerning compensation, work situations, and other employment-related questions as were the practitioners. Instead, these students were asked a limited set of questions about demographic issues, their future plans concerning advanced degrees, their career path interests, and their overall impression of the "health" of the occupational therapy job market.

Modules 7–16: Work Settings

Modules 7–16 contain data specific to each work setting, including a demographic profile, time allocation, compensation, and benefits. The data are more detailed than in other modules to explore, for example, what a person with a specific number of years of experience earns in a specific setting. These modules consist of data tables only and are organized as follows:

- Module 7: Academia
- Module 8: Community
- Module 9: Early Intervention
- Module 10: Freestanding Outpatient
- Module 11: Home Health
- Module 12: Hospital (Non–Mental Health)
- Module 13: Long-Term Care/Skilled-Nursing Facility
- Module 14: Mental Health
- Module 15: Schools
- Module 16: Other Settings.

Project Overview

Introduction

As the professional association for occupational therapy in the United States, the American Occupational Therapy Association (AOTA) continually monitors the occupational therapy profession. Workforce and compensation trends are a key component to the association's efforts and important data for its members. This report presents the results from the *2015 AOTA Salary and Workforce Survey*.

For the first time in some years, the association brought the workforce survey "in house" to have unlimited access to the data received. This increased access will enable more detailed investigation and opportunities to present the data in new, more visual ways in the future. It also will allow for more regular updates, as changes within the profession are occurring at an increasing rate.

Research Methodology

The research process began with an update of the 2010 survey instrument, the most recent in the *AOTA Salary and Workforce Survey* series. Key questions and major classification methods, such as work settings, were retained so that survey data could be accurately tracked over time to ensure analytical consistency.

The balance of the survey was changed to better reflect the multitude of work situations present in the occupational therapy profession. The survey consisted of a variety of modules, each targeting a specific group of respondents:

- **Demographic module**—This module, presented to all practitioners, consisted of baseline issues, such as age, ethnic background, years of experience, educational background, and other broad baseline factors.
- **Self-employment module**—This brief module was presented only to those practitioners who classified themselves as being self-employed in some way.
- **Work setting modules**—Separate modules were created for specific work settings to allow the survey to address questions unique to each setting. All work setting modules collected detailed information concerning compensation and workforce issues specific to that setting. The appropriate module was presented to each respondent according to his or her indication of primary work setting.

- **Benefits module**—This module, presented to all practitioners, collected baseline information concerning the employment benefits received by practitioners.
- **Workforce dynamics module**—This module, presented to all practitioners, explored issues such as job mobility and changes, as well as desire to leave the profession.
- **Student module**—Although students cannot provide information regarding compensation, they are a valuable group to include in a workforce survey to gain insight into the practitioners of the future. Accordingly, this module did not contain compensation questions but rather concentrated on demographic questions, degrees being pursued, future plans, and how challenging or receptive students perceive the occupational therapy job market.

After an initial test in July 2014, AOTA distributed invitation emails beginning in late September and ending in early November 2014 to all people (members, former members, and nonmembers) who had opted in to receive AOTA communications. Three email rounds were used, and the survey remained open for nearly 7 weeks to ensure that all who were interested in participating had the opportunity to do so. All participants were offered a free executive summary of the research results as an incentive to participate in the research program.

Strict confidentiality rules were followed to ensure the data collected remained secure. All contact information submitted to receive the free summary report was housed separately from the survey responses. Additionally, the survey did not collect any detailed information (e.g., employers' names and addresses) that could be used to identify any person or organization. The aggregate data in this report are structured to preserve full respondent anonymity.

Survey Sample and Analytical Techniques

A total of 15,192 people accessed the online form. The data were screened for completeness before analysis. Responses that were extensively incomplete were removed from the sample. Therefore, the total sample was 13,052 participants consisting of 1,273 students, 9,664 OTs, and 2,115 OTAs.

This is the largest sample ever for the survey. The Internet and email have greatly increased response rates. The 2010 survey was the first to use email and generated 11,052 valid responses, and the 2006 survey, which was delivered via mail, had only 3,003 responses (all occupational therapy practitioners, not students).

With any survey, limitations exist regarding the number and level of breakouts possible. Although the overall response volume is highly sound, some subgroups contain relatively few responses and may not be fully representative of that particular segment of the profession. Therefore, the size of each subgroup should be carefully noted before drawing conclusions. Groups with fewer than 100 responses should be interpreted carefully because the data may not be projectable across the entire sample. Groups with fewer than 25 responses should be considered as qualitative data and not projectable.

Past Data Comparisons

When possible and appropriate, historical data are provided to highlight trends. Details on the composition of each of the past samples can be found in the following reports:

- *2010 Occupational Therapy Compensation and Workforce Survey, Final Report*
- *2006 Workforce Survey, Final Report*
- *2000 Compensation Survey, Final Report*
- *1997 Compensation Survey, Final Report.*

Samples before 2006 were limited to AOTA members, with response volumes of 1,812 (1997) and 2,412 (2000). Both the 2010 and 2006 surveys encompass both members and nonmembers and, through their larger scope, are the most analogous sample to the 2014 data. These sampling differences should be considered when examining trends over time.

Data Adjustments and Conversions

The great majority of data provided by the respondents were accepted without change. However, some data points were adjusted as follows:

- **Open-ended responses**—Some questions allowed respondents to select a choice titled "other" and provide an open-ended response. These were reviewed and, when applicable, recoded into a pre-established category to provide for a more-focused and accurate analysis.

- **Outliers**—All compensation data were screened for *outliers* (e.g., very large or very small values). Each was reviewed and, when possible, corrected (cases that involved, e.g., a clearly misplaced decimal point or double entry). Outliers that could not be verified were omitted from the results to avoid skewing the data.

- **Salaried part-time employees**—A small group of 243 (2.1%) respondents stated they were part-time employees but salaried. These participants often did not provide enough information to convert their data into an hourly rate. Given the wide variation in answers, this group was included in demographic summaries but excluded from any further analysis in Module 3, "Compensation Overview," or within their respective work setting compensation profiles.

- **Compensation data**—These data were standardized into annual amounts for full-time employees and hourly amounts for part-time employees (definitions for these categories are provided in Module 3, "Compensation Overview").

Statistical Definitions

The average (also called the *mean*) and the median are used throughout this report to describe the data collected. Although closely related, each summary statistic describes a different facet of the data. The *average* is computed by dividing the sum of all values by the number of values. The *median* is computed by placing all values in numerical order and choosing the value that falls at the midpoint. The average is influenced by outliers; the median is not (Figure O.1). Typically, the median is a more representative indicator of the data when sample sizes are relatively small or when many outliers exist.

Figure O.1. Outliers influence the average but not the median.

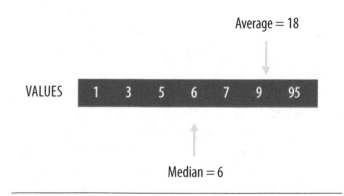

Percentiles are a variation on the median and are especially helpful in interpreting compensation data. Whereas the median splits the data into two equal parts, percentiles go one step further, splitting the data into additional parts. Percentiles are commonly divided into three segments (25th, 50th, and 75th) or five segments (10th, 25th, 50th, 75th, and 90th), with the 50th percentile equal to the median (Figure O.2), but any number of divisions can be made.

Figure O.2. Percentile divided into five segments.

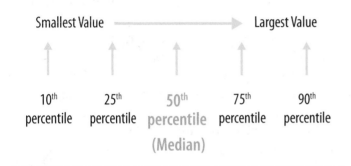

Percentiles help in the interpretation of compensation and related data by providing a concise summation of the distribution of all the data. For example, assume respondents gave the following values for total compensation:

- 10th percentile = $10,000
- 25th percentile = $18,000
- 50th percentile = $45,000
- 75th percentile = $65,000
- 90th percentile = $120,000.

These values show that, although the typical respondent reports a salary of $45,000, the sample includes a wide range of values. One in 10 respondents reports a salary of $10,000 or less; 1 in 10 reports a salary of $120,000 or more. This type of analysis allows for efficient benchmarking to see where a respondent falls in the continuum of responses.

To ensure individual data elements cannot be related to a specific respondent, a full suite of percentiles (10th, 25th, 50th, 75th, and 90th) is provided only when the subsample includes at least 10 responses. A smaller set of percentiles (25th, 50th, and 75th) is provided when the subsample includes 6 to 9 respondents. The median is the only statistic provided when there are 3 to 5 respondents. No data are provided when there are 3 or fewer respondents.

Module 1.
Profile of the Profession

Overview

This module outlines basic demographics for the profession. It explores key metrics, including age, gender, ethnicity, and years of professional experience. It also, in many cases, provides a look into the changing trends within the profession. Although this type of information lacks important probative value (other than interesting statistical "tidbits" on the profession), it is an essential component of the *AOTA Salary and Workforce Survey* because it defines the sample parameters on which all other data are based. These statistics, unless otherwise noted, are based on the 11,779 occupational therapy practitioners who completed the survey. Students are analyzed separately, with their data provided in Module 6.

OT and OTA Status

The vast majority of respondents in this survey were OTs (82%; Figure 1.1). The OTA group of 2,115 (18%) is substantially larger than the 1,384 OTAs covered in the 2010 survey.

Figure 1.1. Number and percentages of OTs and OTAs who completed the survey.

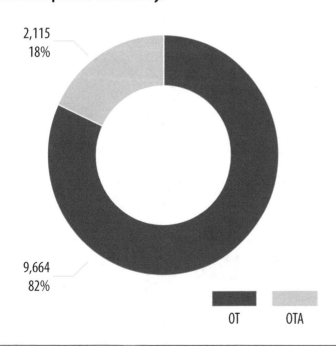

Gender and Age

As in all past studies, women (90.9%) represent the vast majority of respondents (Figure 1.2). Although at its highest point ever, men as a group (8.8%) grew only 0.7% since the last survey. Male OTAs grew more, up from 8.1% in 2010 to 9.4% in 2014 (Figure 1.3).

The median age of survey respondents is 39 years. As in the past, OTs are slightly younger than OTAs (median age 39 vs. 42 years). The overall "aging" trend from 1997 to 2006 seems to have modestly reversed itself. The reversal from 2006 to 2014 is most noteworthy in the growth of the <30 age group and the reduction of the 50–59 group (Table 1.1).

Figure 1.2. Percentages of men and women in the survey.

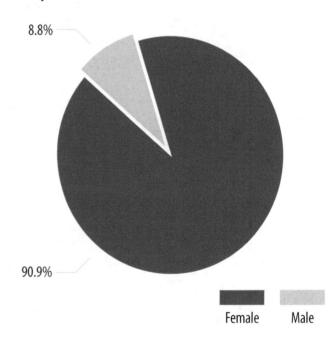

Note: Percentages do not add to 100 due to "Other" and "Prefer not to answer" responses.

Figure 1.3. Percentages of female and male OTs and OTAs in workforce surveys from 1990 to 2014.

OTs

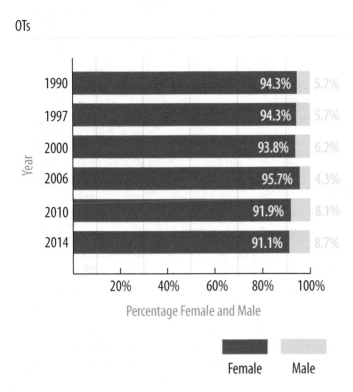

OTAs

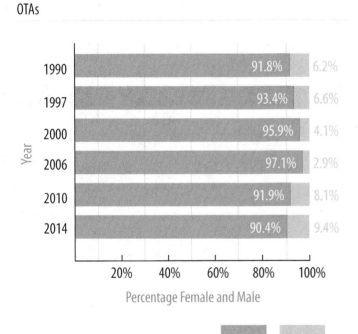

Note: Percentages do not add to 100 due to "Other" and "Prefer not to answer" responses.

Table 1.1. Age of OTs and OTAs

	OTs				
	2014	2010	2006	2000	1997
<30	**23.9%**	17.8%	16.6%	22.0%	20.4%
30–39	**28.9%**	27.8%	27.5%	29.3%	33.5%
40–49	**19.0%**	22.5%	29.2%	32.0%	30.8%
50–59	**19.8%**	25.3%	22.7%	14.1%	11.3%
60–69	**8.1%**	6.1%	3.8%	2.3%	2.9%
70+	**0.3%**	0.4%	0.2%	0.3%	1.2%
Median Age, Yrs	**39**	41	42	39	38

	OTAs				
	2014	2010	2006	2000	1997
<30	**17.5%**	15.7%	7.6%	21.2%	23.4%
30–39	**26.4%**	25.0%	24.1%	27.0%	31.8%
40–49	**24.6%**	25.1%	38.0%	35.8%	32.5%
50–59	**24.5%**	28.9%	25.3%	14.2%	10.6%
60–69	**6.7%**	5.2%	5.1%	1.8%	1.5%
70+	**0.3%**	0.1%	0.0%	0.0%	0.4%
Median Age, Yrs	**42**	43	45	40	37.5

Note: Percentages do not add to 100 due to rounding.

Ethnic Background

Modest change has occurred in ethnic background in the past two surveys. For example, even though respondents who classified themselves as African-American or Black have grown steadily since 2006, up 94%, they still comprise only 3% of the total. This lack of change is seen equally for OTs and OTAs (Table 1.2).

A small age-based differential exists with regard to ethnic background. Interestingly, the 30–39 age group has more ethnic diversity. In the past, the youngest group usually had the most diversity. The differences are small, however, with the large majority of respondents classifying themselves as Caucasian or White regardless of their age cohort (Table 1.3).

Years of Professional Experience

The survey sample comprises respondents with a wide range of experience in the occupational therapy profession. As seen with median age, this survey shows a shift in years of professional experience, with respondents to this survey overall reporting 9 years of professional experience compared with 12 years on the 2010 survey (Table 1.4). The median for OTs went from 12 years in 2010 down to 10 years in this survey, whereas OTAs went from 9 years in 2010 down to 5 years in this survey. This information

is important to consider when comparing cumulative compensation data between the 2010 and 2014 studies. In addition, OTs continue to have more years of experience than OTAs.

Educational Background

The master's degree, for the first time, is now the predominant degree for OTs. Since 2006, the number of OTs with master's degrees has almost doubled, from 31.9% in 2006 to 46.6% in 2010 to 60% in 2014 (Table 1.5). The majority of OTAs continues to practice with an associate's degree (93%), and the percentage with a certificate has dropped from 12.7% in 2006 to 4.8% in 2010 to 3.4% in 2014 (see Table 1.5).

Table 1.6 highlights the changes in educational background since the profession moved to the entry-level master's degree. Smaller, but still of note, is the overall growth in doctoral-level degrees.

Holding degrees outside the occupational therapy field was a trend cited in previous surveys. This trend, especially for those obtaining bachelor's degrees in another field, continues, as more than 50% of OTs have BA and BS degrees in other fields in this survey, a substantial increase from 39.4% in 2010 and 27.7% in 2006 (Table 1.7).

Table 1.2. Ethnic Background of OTs and OTAs

Note: Percentages do not add to 100 due to rounding.

	2014			2010	2006
	Overall	OT	OTA	Overall	Overall
African-American/Black	3.1%	3.0%	3.8%	2.2%	1.6%
American Indian/Alaskan Native	0.3%	0.3%	0.6%	0.3%	0.1%
Asian/Pacific Islander	4.4%	5.1%	1.5%	4.2%	4.7%
Caucasian/White	85.3%	85.3%	85.3%	88.2%	86.2%
Hispanic/Latino	3.2%	2.8%	4.6%	3.9%	1.7%
Multiethnic	1.4%	1.3%	1.9%	1.8%	1.2%
Prefer Not to Answer	2.2%	2.2%	2.4%	3.1%	4.4%

Table 1.3. Ethnic Background of OTs and OTAs by Age

Note: Percentages do not add to 100 due to rounding.

	Overall	20–29	30–39	40–49	50–59	60+
African-American/Black	3.1%	2.6%	3.7%	2.9%	2.9%	2.8%
American Indian/Alaskan Native	0.3%	0.3%	0.2%	0.4%	0.4%	0.2%
Asian/Pacific Islander	4.4%	4.5%	5.9%	4.1%	2.3%	3.6%
Caucasian/White	85.3%	87.4%	82.4%	85.0%	88.2%	88.6%
Hispanic/Latino	3.2%	2.6%	4.0%	4.2%	2.2%	1.4%
Multiethnic	1.4%	1.4%	1.9%	1.5%	1.1%	0.6%
Prefer Not to Answer	2.2%	1.2%	1.9%	1.9%	2.8%	2.8%

Table 1.4. Years of Professional Experience for OTs and OTAs

	10th Percentile	25th Percentile	50th Percentile (Median)	75th Percentile	100th Percentile	Number of Responses
Overall 2000	1.0	3.0	**9.5**	20.0	26.0	2,161
Overall 2006	3.5	6.0	**13.0**	23.0	30.0	2,978
Overall 2010	2.0	5.0	**12.0**	22.1	31.0	9,818
Overall 2014	**1.0**	**3.0**	**9.0**	**19.0**	**30.0**	**11,779**
OT 2014	2.0	4.0	**10.0**	20.0	30.0	9,664
OTA 2014	1.0	2.0	**5.0**	14.0	20.0	2,115

Table 1.5. Degrees Held in the Occupational Therapy Field

	2014 OT	2014 OTA	2010 OT	2010 OTA
Certificate	0.5%	3.4%	0.9%	4.8%
Associate's Degree	0.1%	93.0%	0.2%	91.2%
Baccalaureate Degree	32.0%	1.9%	47.4%	2.5%
Master's Degree	60.0%	0.6%	46.6%	0.9%
Professional Doctorate Degree	4.8%	0.1%	2.7%	0.0%
PhD	1.1%	0.0%	1.3%	0.0%
ScD	0.1%	0.0%	0.1%	0.0%
Other*	0.9%	0.4%	0.5%	0.0%
No Response	0.6%	0.7%	0.2%	0.5%

Note: "Other" refers to degree outside the occupational therapy profession or various certifications other than degrees. Percentages do not add to 100 due to rounding.

Table 1.6. Changes in OT and OTA Educational Background

OTs	2014	2010	2006	2000	1997
Certificate	**0.5%**	0.9%	1.1%	1.2%	1.7%
Associate's Degree	**0.1%**	0.2%	0.3%	0.2%	0.1%
Baccalaureate Degree	**32%**	47.5%	63.8%	62.6%	67.6%
Master's Degree	**60%**	46.6%	31.9%	33.9%	29.5%
Professional Doctorate Degree	**6%**	4.1%	2.4%	2.1%	1.1%

OTAs	2014	2010	2006	2000	1997
Certificate	**3.4%**	4.8%	12.7%	5.4%	2.8%
Associate's Degree	**93%**	91.2%	83.2%	73.1%	80.2%
Baccalaureate Degree	**1.9%**	2.5%	2.5%	19.0%	16.0%
Master's Degree	**0.6%**	0.9%	0.0%	2.5%	1.0%
Professional Doctorate Degree	**0.1%**	0.0%	0.0%	0.0%	0.0%

Note: Data for 1997 and 2000 indicate the highest degree held in any field. Data from 2006 onward indicate the highest degree held in the occupational therapy field. Percentages do not add to 100 due to rounding.

Table 1.7. Degrees Held Outside the Occupational Therapy Field

	2014 OT	2014 OTA	2010 OT	2010 OTA
Associate's Degree	6.5%	24.2%	7.2%	18.4%
BA/BS Degree	50.5%	25.1%	39.4%	20.7%
Master's Degree (e.g., MBA, MPH, MEd)	11.9%	2.9%	12.3%	2.3%
EdD	0.5%	0.0%	0.5%	0.1%
ScD	0.0%	0.0%	0.0%	0.0%
PhD	1.5%	0.0%	1.9%	0.1%
Other	2.3%	2.9%	0.3%	0.0%
No Degree Held Outside the Occupational Therapy Field/No Reponse	0.0%	33.2%	42.9%	60.8%

Note: Percentages do not add to 100% because the respondents could select more than one degree. "Other" encompasses a variety of certifications and degrees such as doctor of chiropractic, doctor of physical therapy, MD, JD, and EdS.

Advanced Practice Certifications and Recognitions

Obtaining an advanced practice certification or recognition (e.g., certified hand therapist, board certified in pediatrics, board certified in neurorehabilitation) continues to slightly decline, with an overall drop from 21.9% in 2010 to 18.6% in 2014 (Figure 1.4). The drop is mainly among OTs, with OTAs having only dropped slightly. The likelihood of holding advanced certification increases with years of experience and for those employed in a freestanding outpatient setting (Table 1.8).

State Licensure

In answer to the question "In how many states do you hold a current license to work as an occupational therapy practitioner?" the majority of respondents (82.4%) indicated only one state (Table 1.9). The most popular states as work locations are

- New York (5.7%)
- California (5.7%)
- Ohio (5.6%)
- Illinois (5.3%)
- Texas (4.7%)
- Pennsylvania (4.3%).

Classifying the work locations by region shows that respondents are most often located in the North Central and Northeast regions, with these two areas collectively accounting for the majority of the responses (Figure 1.5).

Figure 1.4. Advanced practice certifications and recognitions.

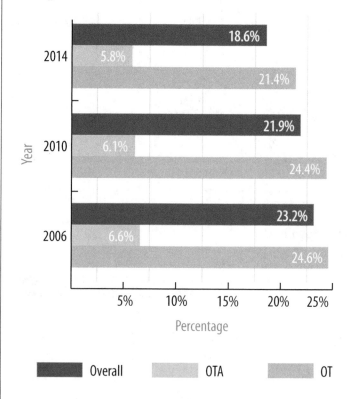

Figure 1.5. Regional distribution of occupational therapy practitioners.

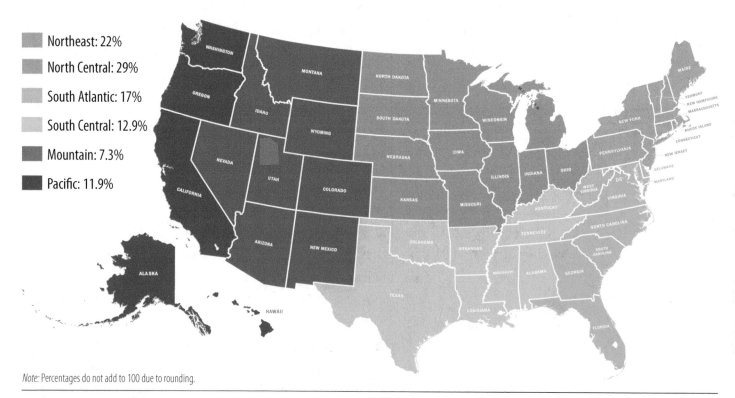

- Northeast: 22%
- North Central: 29%
- South Atlantic: 17%
- South Central: 12.9%
- Mountain: 7.3%
- Pacific: 11.9%

Note: Percentages do not add to 100 due to rounding.

Table 1.8. Prevalence of Advanced Practice Certifications and Recognitions

		Currently Hold	Currently Pursuing	Plan to Start in the New Year	No Plans to Start	No Response
Overall	Overall 2000	15.4%	6.1%	13.8%	64.7%	0.0%
	Overall 2006	23.2%	4.9%	13.4%	57.6%	0.9%
	Overall 2010	21.9%	5.7%	15.7%	56.3%	0.4%
	Overall 2014	**18.6%**	**5.2%**	**18.2%**	**58.0%**	**0.0%**
OT/OTA Status, 2014	OT	21.4%	5.5%	17.1%	56.0%	0.0%
	OTA	5.8%	3.7%	23.5%	67.7%	0.0%
Years of Professional Experience, 2014	0–5	12.2%	47.7%	59.0%	36.1%	0.0%
	5.1–10	13.2%	23.8%	17.3%	16.8%	0.0%
	10.1–15	14.4%	11.4%	8.9%	14.1%	0.0%
	15.1–25	27.7%	11.9%	10.6%	19.3%	0.0%
	25+	32.5%	5.2%	4.3%	13.7%	0.0%
Entry-Level Degree, 2014	Associate's Degree	6.4%	3.8%	23.8%	66.6%	0.0%
	Baccalaureate Degree	33.1%	3.5%	8.7%	54.7%	0.0%
	Master's Degree	13.6%	6.8%	22.6%	57.0%	0.0%
	Professional Doctorate Degree	15.0%	10.3%	23.8%	50.9%	0.0%
	PhD	37.5%	4.3%	4.2%	54.2%	0.0%
Primary Work Setting, 2014	Academia	29.9%	2.9%	8.2%	59.1%	0.0%
	Community	21.7%	6.6%	15.9%	55.8%	0.0%
	Early Intervention	20.4%	5.4%	20.6%	53.7%	0.0%
	Freestanding Outpatient	33.8%	10.2%	17.6%	38.5%	0.0%
	Home Health	18.2%	5.7%	13.8%	62.4%	0.0%
	Hospital (Non–Mental Health)	22.5%	6.5%	19.7%	51.3%	0.0%
	LTC/SNF	8.0%	4.1%	23.2%	64.7%	0.0%
	Mental Health	5.4%	3.5%	20.7%	70.5%	0.0%
	Schools	17.1%	3.0%	13.8%	66.1%	0.0%
	Other	31.3%	5.5%	14.8%	48.4%	0.0%

Note: Percentages do not add to 100 due to rounding.

Table 1.9. Number of States Where License Is Held

	2014	2010
One	82.4%	85.1%
Two	11.4%	11.4%
Three	2.5%	1.7%
Four	0.7%	0.4%
Five or More	0.3%	0.3%
None or No Response	0.4%	1.0%

AOTA Membership Status

The majority of respondents (58.6%) are current AOTA members. More than one-third (37.2%) are former members, with the remaining 4.2% indicating they have never been a member (Figure 1.6).

The differences among respondents who are current AOTA members, former members, and nonmembers are explored in Table 1.10. For example, current members are older than former members and nonmembers. Substantial variations exist, especially among the nonmembers.

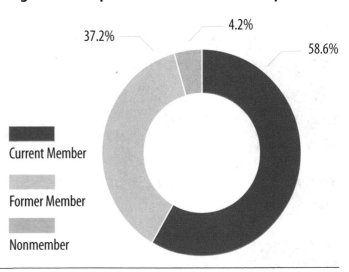

Figure 1.6. Respondents' AOTA membership status.

- Current Member
- Former Member
- Nonmember

37.2% 4.2% 58.6%

Table 1.10. Current and Former AOTA Member and Nonmember Respondent Demographics

Note: Percentages do not add to 100 due to rounding.

		Current Members	Former Members	Nonmembers
	Sample Size	6,905	4,375	499
	Median Age, Years	42	36	37
OT/OTA Status	OT	61.2%	35.8%	3.1%
	OTA	47.0%	43.3%	9.7%
Gender	Female	88.6%	91.2%	88.6%
	Male	10.8%	8.5%	10.2%
Ethnic Background	African-American/Black	2.8%	3.5%	3.2%
	American Indian/Alaskan Native	0.4%	0.3%	0.2%
	Asian/Pacific Islander	4.6%	4.4%	3.8%
	Caucasian/White	85.6%	85.0%	84.6%
	Hispanic/Latino	3.0%	3.4%	3.8%
	Multiethnic	1.5%	1.5%	0.8%
Highest Degree Held in the Occupational Therapy Field	Certificate	1.0%	1.0%	0.6%
	Associate's Degree	13.3%	19.6%	39.0%
	Baccalaureate Degree	29.0%	23.3%	22.2%
	Master's Degree	47.9%	35.8%	35.3%
	Professional Doctorate Degree	1.0%	2.1%	0.8%
	PhD	1.4%	0.0%	0.0%
	ScD	0.1%	0.1%	0.2%
Advanced Practice Certification/Recognition in Occupational Therapy	Yes, Have Achieved One or More	21.3%	15.2%	10.8%
	Currently Pursuing	5.2%	5.4%	3.8%
	Plan to Start the Process	18.8%	17.7%	14.6%

Module 2.
Work Setting Overview and Profile

Overview

This module is centered on work setting issues. In addition to exploring where the respondents work, this module explores some key workforce issues such as

- Organizational and ownership status of respondents' employers
- Prevalence of self-employment in the profession
- Prevalence of working in multiple settings.

More detailed information on each specific setting is provided in Modules 7–16.

In 2010, the work setting list used was modified to allow for additional, focused analyses for key sectors and to better reflect changes in work settings seen in the past. The major change involved splitting the Early Intervention/School setting into two components (Early Intervention and Schools). This approach allows the survey to explore issues unique to each of these settings.

Although these changes are beneficial for the 2014 analysis, it does place some constraints on how the current survey can be compared with studies from 2006 and earlier. Instances in which the setting categories have been altered from past *AOTA Workforce Surveys* are noted as such in the affected tables. Keep these setting differences in mind when drawing conclusions from the data. Exhibit 2.1 shows the 2014 work settings, along with key examples.

Primary Work Setting

As seen in past studies, occupational therapy practitioners are found in a wide range of work settings (Table 2.1). However, three work settings account for a majority of responses: Hospital (Non–Mental Health), Schools, and Long-Term Care (LTC)/Skilled-Nursing Facility (SNF). Collectively, these three settings account for more than two-thirds of the respondents (68.7%) describing their primary work setting (i.e., the setting where they spend the greatest share of their work hours).

Substantial work setting differences exist based on whether the respondent is an OT or an OTA. OTAs are more likely than ever to be working at a LTC/SNF, with this setting accounting for 55.9% of the OTA respondents

(up from 45% in 2010). In contrast, 19.2% of the OTs identified a LTC/SNF setting as their primary setting; however, this setting was the fastest growing for both OTs and OTAs. Overall patterns are similar to those seen in previous studies, with a slow movement toward LTC/SNF and away from other traditional settings. Responses differentiated by OT and OTA status are provided in Table 2.2.

Primary Work Setting Location

Respondents now most commonly describe an urban setting as their primary work setting location, selected by 42.5%. A suburban setting closely follows an urban setting with 39.7% response. About 18% of respondents are employed at a primary work setting located in a rural area (Figure 2.1). Responses based on OT and OTA status show that OTs are slightly more likely to work in an urban setting, whereas OTAs are moving from rural and suburban settings toward urban settings (Table 2.3).

Classifying work setting location by work setting shows patterns consistent with those seen in past *AOTA Workforce Studies* (Table 2.4). Academia, Hospital (Non–Mental Health), and Mental Health settings are most likely to be in an urban environment—the majority of respondents employed in these settings described their location as urban. The Home Health setting has the highest concentration of rural locations, at 23%.

Exhibit 2.1. 2014 Work Settings and Examples

Academia
- College/university, 4 year or more
- College, 2 year

Community
- Adult day care program
- Area agency on aging
- Community residential care facility
- Environmental modification program/services
- Group home
- Independent-living center
- Low vision program
- Prevention/wellness program
- Retirement/assisted living
- Senior center
- Supervised housing

Early Intervention
- Early intervention program
- Early intervention—private practice
- Pediatric day care program

Freestanding Outpatient
- Comprehensive outpatient rehab facility
- Physician/optometrist
- Private practice—office based
- Rehabilitation agency/clinic
- Not-for-profit agency

Home Health
- Home health agency—freestanding
- Home health care—hospital based
- Mobile treatment team/home care

Hospital (Non–Mental Health)
- General hospital—acute, inpatient
- Hospice—general hospital
- Hospital-based outpatient services
- Neonatal intensive care unit
- Pediatric unit—general hospital
- Rehabilitation hospital—freestanding
- Rehabilitation unit—general hospital

LTC/SNF
- Hospital—subacute unit
- LTC facility—no skilled beds
- SNF—non-skilled unit
- SNF—skilled or subacute unit

Mental Health
- Behavioral health—freestanding
- Behavioral health—general hospital
- Partial hospitalization program (community based, not outpatient)
- Partial hospitalization unit—general hospital
- Mental health day program

Schools
- School system (includes private schools)
- Transitional program for high school students

Other
- Driving program
- Industrial rehab/work programs
- Sheltered workshop
- Supported employment
- Any other setting not listed here

Table 2.1. Primary Work Setting Trends

Note: Percentages do not add to 100 due to rounding.

	2014	2010	2006	2000
Academia	**5.3%**	5.2%	5.7%	6.2%
Community	**1.9%**	2.0%	1.6%	2.1%
Early Intervention	**4.3%**	4.8%	*(included with Schools)*	
Freestanding Outpatient	**9.8%**	9.3%	10.6%	8.1%
Home Health	**6.3%**	5.8%	6.9%	6.0%
Hospital (Non–Mental Health)	**23.9%**	26.2%	23.0%	26.2%
LTC/SNF	**25.8%**	19.9%	17.0%	15.9%
Mental Health	**2.2%**	2.9%	3.6%	4.7%
Schools	**19.0%**	21.6%	29.6%	29.0%
Other	**1.6%**	2.3%	1.9%	1.9%

Table 2.2. Primary Work Setting Trends by OT and OTA Status

Note: Percentages do not add to 100 due to rounding.

	OT				OTA			
	2014	2010	2006	2000	**2014**	2010	2006	2000
Academia	**6.1%**	5.8%	6.1%	6.6%	**1.5%**	1.8%	1.7%	2.9%
Community	**2.0%**	1.8%	1.6%	2.2%	**1.7%**	3.1%	2.1%	2.0%
Early Intervention	**4.6%**	5.2%	(included with Schools)		**2.8%**	1.8%	(included with Schools)	
Freestanding Outpatient	**10.8%**	10.2%	11.2%	11.6%	**5.3%**	4.3%	3.3%	8.3%
Home Health	**6.8%**	5.9%	7.2%	6.6%	**4.3%**	4.8%	3.3%	1.7%
Hospital (Non–Mental Health)	**26.6%**	28.1%	23.5%	24.6%	**11.3%**	14.4%	17.5%	13.6%
LTC/SNF	**19.2%**	15.8%	15.4%	12.9%	**55.9%**	45.0%	36.3%	38.4%
Mental Health	**2.4%**	3.0%	3.6%	5.2%	**1.4%**	2.4%	4.2%	5.4%
Schools	**19.9%**	21.7%	29.6%	29.2%	**15.2%**	21.4%	29.6%	26.0%
Other	**1.7%**	2.5%	1.9%	1.7%	**0.9%**	1.1%	2.1%	1.7%

Figure 2.1. Primary work setting location.

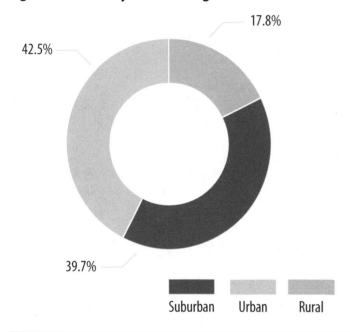

42.5%

17.8%

39.7%

Suburban Urban Rural

Table 2.3. Primary Work Setting Location Trends

	OT				
	2014	2010	2006	2000	1997
Urban	**43.4%**	39.0%	36.9%	43.1%	43.0%
Suburban	**39.9%**	42.4%	41.7%	39.2%	37.1%
Rural	**16.7%**	18.3%	19.9%	17.8%	19.8%

	OTA				
	2014	2010	2006	2000	1997
Urban	**37.2%**	27.6%	27.9%	35.2%	38.7%
Suburban	**40.6%**	44.7%	43.4%	41.1%	39.1%
Rural	**22.3%**	27.2%	25.8%	23.7%	22.2%

Note: Percentages do not add to 100 due to rounding.

Table 2.4. Work Setting Location by Work Setting

		Urban	Suburban	Rural
Academia	**2014**	**58.3%**	**28.4%**	**13.5%**
	2010	56.7%	27.7%	15.0%
	2006	57.3%	26.3%	16.4%
	2000	62.1%	21.2%	16.7%
Community	**2014**	**43.4%**	**46.5%**	**10.2%**
	2010	39.9%	46.0%	14.1%
	2006	36.7%	44.9%	18.4%
	2000	43.8%	35.6%	20.5%

(Continued)

Table 2.4. Work Setting Location by Work Setting *(cont.)*

		Urban	Suburban	Rural
Early Intervention	**2014**	**41.0%**	**42.8%**	**16.2%**
	2010	35.8%	44.7%	19.1%
	2006			
	2000	*Included with Schools for until 2006.*		
Freestanding Outpatient	**2014**	**41.5%**	**46.5%**	**12.1%**
	2010	36.5%	49.7%	13.5%
	2006	32.8%	52.4%	13.6%
	2000	43.9%	41.4%	14.6%
Home Health	**2014**	**34.4%**	**42.5%**	**23.1%**
	2010	26.3%	46.7%	27.0%
	2006	30.6%	45.1%	21.8%
	2000	40.2%	40.2%	19.7%
Hospital (Non–Mental Health)	**2014**	**56.3%**	**29.1%**	**14.7%**
	2010	51.8%	31.5%	16.4%
	2006	51.7%	30.9%	16.1%
	2000	55.0%	31.3%	13.7%
LTC/SNF	**2014**	**34.4%**	**43.5%**	**22.1%**
	2010	25.8%	49.1%	24.7%
	2006	28.0%	44.3%	26.9%
	2000	29.3%	44.0%	26.6%
Mental Health	**2014**	**61.5%**	**28.9%**	**9.6%**
	2010	57.9%	27.0%	14.7%
	2006	55.6%	28.7%	13.9%
	2000	55.4%	30.4%	14.3%
Schools (Includes Early Intervention Until 2006)	**2014**	**32.5%**	**46.8%**	**20.7%**
	2010	25.6%	52.2%	22.0%
	2006	24.1%	49.6%	24.2%
	2000	31.5%	48.6%	19.9%
Other	**2014**	**48.6%**	**36.3%**	**15.4%**
	2010	47.4%	37.4%	14.3%
	2006	48.2%	35.7%	12.5%
	2000	*Included with Community setting before 2000.*		

Note: Percentages do not add to 100 due to rounding.

AOTA Members and Nonmembers by Work Setting

Figures 2.2 and 2.3 examine the differences between AOTA members and nonmembers by work setting to answer the question "Does AOTA membership reflect the composition of the profession according to work setting?" Respondents indicate that AOTA membership is more common for those in Academia and slightly less common for those in LTC/SNF. In the remaining settings, work setting is not a predictor of membership. For instance, 8.8% of member respondents identified themselves in Academia vs. only 0.4% of the nonmember group. Conversely, LTC/SNF totaled 30.7% of nonmember responses vs. 22.4% of members.

Figure 2.2. AOTA members by work setting.

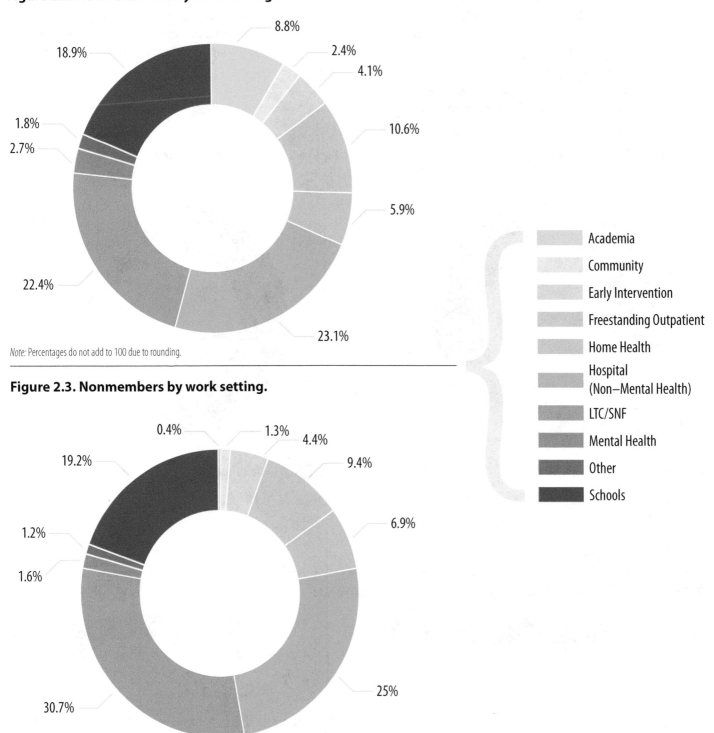

Note: Percentages do not add to 100 due to rounding.

Figure 2.3. Nonmembers by work setting.

Note: Percentages do not add to 100 due to rounding.

Primary Work Setting Control and Ownership

Private for-profit control and ownership structure is the most popular response by a small margin when the respondents describe the type of control and ownership for their primary work setting. Private nonprofits are also highly popular, with government settings the least common (Figure 2.4).

OTs are closely divided between private for profit setting (36.5%) and private nonprofit (32.2%). For the first time, in this survey participants were given the choice of "Unsure" about the type of control or ownership, which accounts for 7.4% of responses.

The data in Figure 2.4 and Table 2.5 exclude respondents who are employed in the Academia setting. Those employed in Academia were asked instead to indicate whether their institution is public or private. As summarized in Figure 2.5, public institutions are slightly more common than private institutions.

Time Allocation

Practitioners, except those in Academia, were asked to indicate the average percentage of time they spent at their primary work setting in five functional areas. Figure 2.6 is a summary for all work settings (except Academia). Figure 2.7 details results by each work setting. LTC/SNF had the highest amount of time dedicated to direct client intervention and the lowest amount for indirect and administration. Research was closely distributed in the 3%–6% range across work settings.

Figure 2.4. Primary work setting.

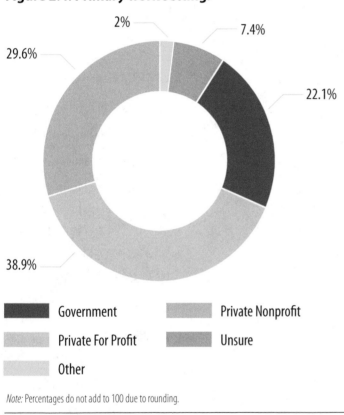

- Government
- Private For Profit
- Other
- Private Nonprofit
- Unsure

Note: Percentages do not add to 100 due to rounding.

Figure 2.5. Type of academic institution.

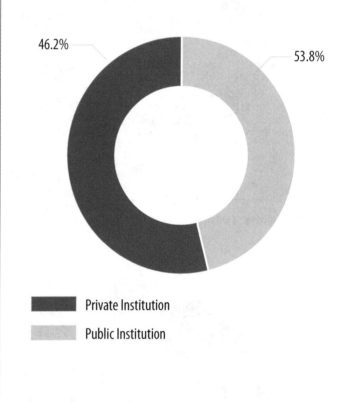

- Private Institution
- Public Institution

Table 2.5. Primary Work Setting Control and Ownership Trends

	OT						OTA				
	2014	2010	2006	2000	1997		**2014**	2010	2006	2000	1997
Government	**23.6%**	26.5%	29.4%	35.0%	28.3%	Government	**15.6%**	20.0%	23.8%	30.3%	24.1%
Private For Profit	**36.5%**	35.9%	34.5%	32.7%	38.5%	Private For Profit	**49.7%**	51.1%	40.2%	42.4%	52.1%
Private Nonprofit	**32.2%**	35.5%	33.9%	32.3%	33.2%	Private Nonprofit	**18.3%**	25.5%	33.2%	27.3%	23.8%
Unsure/Other	**7.4%**					Unsure/Other	**16.5%**				

Note: Percentages do not add to 100 due to rounding.

Figure 2.6. Time allocation for all work settings.

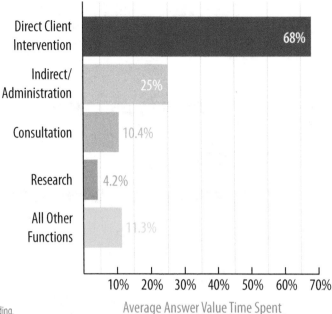

Direct Client Intervention	68%
Indirect/ Administration	25%
Consultation	10.4%
Research	4.2%
All Other Functions	11.3%

Average Answer Value Time Spent

Note: Percentages do not add to 100 due to rounding.

Figure 2.7. Time allocation by work setting.

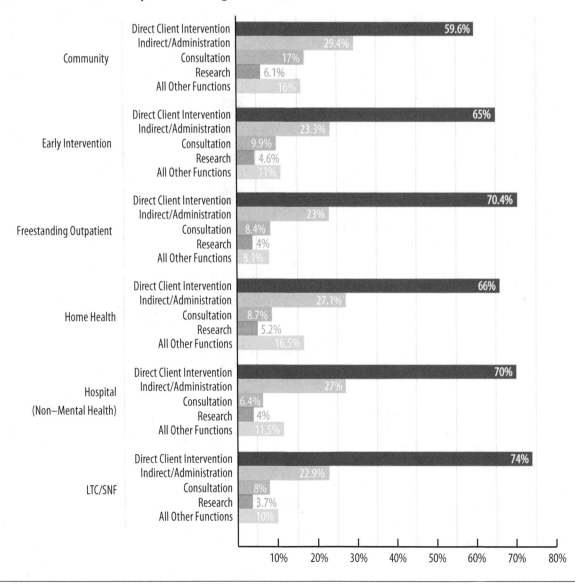

Community
- Direct Client Intervention 59.6%
- Indirect/Administration 29.4%
- Consultation 17%
- Research 6.1%
- All Other Functions 16%

Early Intervention
- Direct Client Intervention 65%
- Indirect/Administration 23.3%
- Consultation 9.9%
- Research 4.6%
- All Other Functions 11%

Freestanding Outpatient
- Direct Client Intervention 70.4%
- Indirect/Administration 23%
- Consultation 8.4%
- Research 4%
- All Other Functions 8.1%

Home Health
- Direct Client Intervention 66%
- Indirect/Administration 27.1%
- Consultation 8.7%
- Research 5.2%
- All Other Functions 16.5%

Hospital (Non–Mental Health)
- Direct Client Intervention 70%
- Indirect/Administration 27%
- Consultation 6.4%
- Research 4%
- All Other Functions 11.5%

LTC/SNF
- Direct Client Intervention 74%
- Indirect/Administration 22.9%
- Consultation 8%
- Research 3.7%
- All Other Functions 10%

(Continued)

Figure 2.7. Time allocation by work setting *(cont.)*.

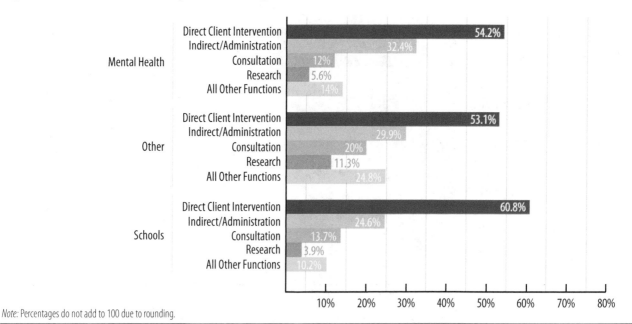

Note: Percentages do not add to 100 due to rounding.

Self-Employment and Contractual Work

Self-employment, either full- or part-time, seems to be declining. Responses based on OT and OTA status show roughly the same trends. The majority (80.1% of OTs and 85.9% of OTAs) stated they are not self-employed or paid on a contractual basis, which is an 11% decrease for both (Figure 2.8).

Data on the prevalence of self-employment date back to 1973. As summarized in Table 2.6, self-employment levels (for all or some work in the profession) dropped greatly over more recent years for both OTs and OTAs.

Secondary Work Settings

The majority of the survey questions targeted the respondents' primary work setting because this setting accounts for the greatest share of their work time. However, it is well known from past AOTA studies that multiple work settings are not uncommon.

The percentage of respondents who indicated they work at a secondary setting has dropped slightly, about 3% overall since 2010 (i.e., from 31.1% in 2010 to 28.3% in 2014). The responses have remained fairly constant based on OT or OTA status and drop somewhat among those with 10 to 15 years of professional experience. The greatest variation among respondents is in the primary setting, with the prevalence of working at an additional setting highest among those in Academia and School settings (Table 2.7).

LTC/SNF is the most cited secondary setting (32.8%) and is especially noteworthy among OTAs, who cited it more than 50% of the time. Hospital (Non–Mental Health) and Home Health are also popular secondary settings among both OTs and OTAs (Table 2.8).

Respondents reported that they worked a median of 6 hours per week at their secondary work setting. Additional details on hours worked and the impact on total compensation are provided in Module 3, Table 3.17.

Figure 2.8. Self-employment and contractual work.

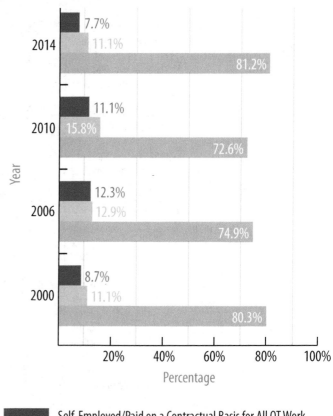

- ■ Self-Employed/Paid on a Contractual Basis for All OT Work
- ■ Self-Employed/Paid on a Contractual Basis for Some OT Work
- ■ Not Self-Employed or Paid on a Contractual Basis

Note: Percentages do not add to 100 due to rounding.

Table 2.6. Long-Term Self-Employment Trends

	2014	2010	2006	2000	1997	1996	1990	1986	1982	1977	1973
OT	**19.9%**	28.1%	25.9%	21.2%	21.7%	23.1%	26.4%	19.5%	15%	12.3%	6.0%
OTA	**14.1%**	23.1%	16.4%	7.4%	11.1%	10.2%	11.3%	6.1%	4.0%	8.0%	3.4%

Note: Data are the percentage of respondents who are self-employed on either a full-time (i.e., their sole work situation) or a part-time (i.e., a work situation in addition to others) basis.

Table 2.7. Percentage of Respondents Working at a Secondary Setting

	Overall	**28.3%**
OT/OTA Status	OT	28.7%
	OTA	26.5%
	0–5	35.9%
	5.1–10	18.7%
Years of Professional Experience	10.1–15	13.8%
	15.1–25	17.0%
	25+	14.6%
	Academia	39.6%
	Community	30.4%
	Early Intervention	27.5%
	Freestanding Outpatient	28.2%
	Home Health	28.3%
Primary Setting	Hospital (Non–Mental Health)	23.7%
	LTC/SNF	26.0%
	Mental Health	26.3%
	Schools	34.2%
	Other	27.2%

Note: Percentages do not add to 100 due to rounding.

Table 2.8. Secondary Work Settings

	Overall	OT	OTA
Academia	**8.2%**	8.8%	4.3%
Community	**4.3%**	4.6%	3.1%
Early Intervention	**8.8%**	9.4%	5.5%
Freestanding Outpatient	**11.3%**	12.1%	7.4%
Home Health	**16.7%**	16.2%	19.7%
Hospital (Non–Mental Health)	**20.1%**	20.6%	17.4%
LTC/SNF	**32.8%**	29.2%	50.3%
Mental Health	**2.0%**	2.1%	1.7%
Schools	**8.3%**	8.5%	6.9%
Other	**5.6%**	6.4%	1.7%

Note: Percentages do not add to 100 because respondents could indicate more than one secondary setting.

Module 3.
Compensation Overview

Overview

This module covers the core focus of the survey—how much do those in the occupational therapy profession earn, how much do they work, how are they compensated, and how have these elements changed over the years? These questions appear to be simple to answer, but given the enormous variety of work settings and situations, developing accurate answers is complicated.

Compensation data are explored in two basic formats. This module provides overview data, classifying respondents by overarching metrics such as work classification (e.g., part-time vs. full-time), years of experience, location, work setting, and others. Each metric is examined independently for OTs and OTAs. These data are intended to provide a broad overview of compensation practices in the profession and explore how compensation is affected by key metrics.

More detailed data are provided in Modules 7–16, which explore compensation (among other factors) for each individual work setting. Within each setting, the data are broken out by multiple metrics to examine, for example, what an OT working in the Community setting who has a certain number of years of experience earns. Both the overview data in this module and the detailed data in Modules 7–16 explore different, but equally important, facets of the compensation landscape.

In addition to base compensation, this module explores the prevalence of additional cash compensation, such as bonus monies, stipends, and other such income. Compensation data are also provided for secondary work settings among respondents who indicated they were employed in more than one setting.

Work Week Hours in Primary Work Setting

Before examining compensation, it is necessary to organize the data according to how many hours a person works in a typical week in the primary work setting. To ensure consistency with past studies, the same classification system is used, consisting of the following three groups:

- **Full-time**—People who work 30 or more hours per week at their primary setting. Their compensation data are provided as an annual salary.
- **Standard part-time**—People who work 11–29 hours per week at their primary setting. Their compensation data are provided as an hourly value.
- **Limited part-time**—People who work 10 or fewer hours per week at their primary setting. Their compensation data are provided as an hourly value.

In the 2010 survey, there was a marked increase in the number of full-time workers. Although that trend seems to be holding, there is a notable downward shift in the number of full-time and a notable upward shift in part-time OTAs in from 2010 to 2014. However, as summarized in Table 3.1, a large majority of both OTs and OTAs fall into the full-time category for their primary work setting.

Although no change has occurred in the overall median number of hours worked per week, a reduction in the number of hours worked has occurred at both the low and high end of the spectrum. The 10th percentile in 2010 was 25 hours and is now 20 hours. The same change occurred in the 90th percentile, decreasing from 45 hours to 40 hours, suggesting that less than 40 hours is becoming more common for full-time status. Still, the "typical" respondent continues putting in a 40-hour work week at the primary work setting (Table 3.2).

Hourly compensation vs. receiving a salary increased for both OTs and OTAs. Salaried OTs decreased by 10% and represent less than 50% of the workforce for the first time. The same trend holds true for OTAs. With more practitioners working in Hospitals and LTC/SNF, where hourly compensation is most common, an overall shift away from salaried working arrangements has occurred in primary work settings (Table 3.3).

Table 3.1. Work Week Hours

	Overall			OT			OTA		
	1–10	11–29	30+	1–10	11–29	30+	1–10	11–29	30+
2014	**3.3%**	**14.3%**	**82.5%**	**3.1%**	**14.0%**	**82.9%**	**3.8%**	**15.6%**	**80.7%**
2010	1.9%	13.3%	84.8%	1.9%	13.5%	84.6%	2.1%	11.9%	86.0%
2006	3.4%	18.6%	78.0%	3.4%	19.0%	77.6%	3.8%	14.2%	82.1%
2000	4.2%	27.0%	68.8%	4.3%	27.2%	68.5%	4.2%	25.3%	70.5%

Note: Percentages do not add to 100 due to rounding.

Table 3.2. Hours Worked in a Typical Week

	Number of Responses 2014	10th Percentile 2014	25th Percentile 2014	**50th Percentile (Median) 2014**	75th Percentile 2014	90th Percentile 2014	Median 2010	Median 2006	Median 2000
Overall	11,154	20	34	**40**	40	40	40	40	35
OT	9,070	20	32	**40**	40	45	40	40	35
OTA	2084	20	32	**40**	40	40	40	40	35

Note: Percentages do not add to 100 due to rounding.

Table 3.3. Compensation Method

	OT					OTA			
	2014	2010	2006	2000		**2014**	2010	2006	2000
Salary	**48.7%**	54.4%	52.1%	55.2%	Salary	**11.8%**	19.9%	32.8%	29.1%
Hourly	**44.7%**	39.4%	37.5%	35.1%	Hourly	**83.6%**	75.3%	60.7%	68.5%
By Service (fee for service)	**6.4%**	6.2%	9.3%	9.7%	By Service (fee for service)	**4.7%**	4.8%	4.5%	3.4%

Note: Responses for 2010 and 2014 exclude those in Academia. Percentages do not add to 100 due to rounding.

Compensation Overview

The compensation data examination begins by addressing the most broad-based question: Overall, regardless of work setting, years of experience, or other factors, what do occupational therapy practitioners earn? As summarized in Table 3.4, the "typical" OT working full-time earned $70,000 in 2014, an 8.2% increase from the 2010 survey. Those working part-time earned $44.00 per hour (for a standard part-time schedule) or $45.00 per hour (for a limited part-time schedule). For OTAs, these same values are $48,000 (full-time), $28.00 per hour (for a standard part-time schedule), and $30.00 per hour (for a limited part-time schedule).

Tables 3.5–3.10 explore overall annual salary data for OTs and OTAs according to the following key factors:

- Table 3.5. Total years of experience in the profession
- Table 3.6. Region of the country and work setting location
- Table 3.7. Highest degree held in the occupational therapy profession
- Table 3.8. AOTA membership status
- Table 3.9. State where employed
- Table 3.10. Primary work setting.

For each table, data include the base annual salary earned at the primary work setting for a full-time schedule.

Table 3.4. Annual Salary Overview

		10th Percentile	25th Percentile	50th Percentile (Median)	75th Percentile	90th Percentile	Number of Responses
OT	Full-Time	$50,000	$60,000	**$70,000**	$81,000	$95,000	8,087
	Standard Part-Time	$31.00	$37.00	**$44.00**	$50.00	$60.00	1,283
	Limited Part-Time	$32.10	$40.00	**$45.00**	$55.00	$71.80	294
OTA	Full-Time	$33,000	$40,000	**$48,000**	$56,000	$65,000	1,707
	Standard Part-Time	$20.00	$24.00	**$28.00**	$34.00	$37.00	328
	Limited Part-Time	$20.00	$25.00	**$30.00**	$33.75	$35.00	80

Note: Data include only base salary compensation received at the primary setting.

Table 3.5. Annual Salary Overview by Total Years of Experience

		10th Percentile	25th Percentile	50th Percentile (Median)	75th Percentile	90th Percentile	Number of Responses
OT	0–1 Years	$40,000	$51,125	**$59,000**	$68,000	$75,000	392
	1.1–2 Years	$45,550	$53,000	**$60,000**	$68,000	$76,900	811
	2.1–4 Years	$48,076	$55,000	**$62,000**	$70,000	$80,000	1,209
	4.1–6 Years	$50,000	$59,000	**$65,000**	$75,000	$85,000	896
	6.1–9 Years	$54,800	$62,000	**$69,000**	$80,000	$90,000	757
	9.1–14 Years	$52,000	$62,000	**$72,000**	$83,000	$93,000	987
	14.1–20 Years	$53,000	$64,000	**$75,000**	$87,000	$96,482	1,140
	20.1–25 Years	$58,000	$67,250	**$78,000**	$91,000	$106,900	579
	25+ Years	$58,000	$69,000	**$80,000**	$93,234	$108,000	1,316
OTA	0–1 Years	$29,526	$37,250	**$39,000**	$50,922	$56,900	104
	1.1–2 Years	$28,550	$38,250	**$42,000**	$50,000	$56,900	217
	2.1–4 Years	$31,100	$39,000	**$45,000**	$52,000	$60,000	380
	4.1–6 Years	$31,100	$40,000	**$47,000**	$56,000	$65,000	202
	6.1–9 Years	$35,000	$40,000	**$48,000**	$54,250	$67,700	219
	9.1–14 Years	$36,000	$45,000	**$50,000**	$60,000	$69,000	167
	14.1–20 Years	$34,000	$40,000	**$50,000**	$58,000	$70,800	221
	20.1–25 Years	$38,943	$45,125	**$55,000**	$68,000	$77,678	104
	25+ Years	$35,100	$42,000	**$48,750**	$62,000	$71,950	93

Table 3.6. Annual Salary Overview by Region and Work Setting Location

			10th Percentile	25th Percentile	50th Percentile (Median)	75th Percentile	90th Percentile	Number of Responses
OT	Region	Northeast	$48,000	$59,000	$68,000	$80,000	$92,000	1,821
		South Atlantic	$50,000	$60,000	$70,000	$82,000	$93,960	1,417
		South Central	$52,000	$60,000	$70,000	$83,000	$96,000	1,056
		North Central	$48,000	$56,000	$65,000	$77,000	$89,494	2,231
		Mountain	$42,100	$55,000	$66,000	$79,000	$91,900	564
		Pacific	$50,000	$63,000	$75,000	$89,000	$100,000	998
	Work Setting Location	Urban	$50,000	$60,000	$69,000	$81,000	$95,000	3,608
		Suburban	$48,000	$58,000	$68,000	$80,395	$93,000	3,132
		Rural	$45,000	$56,000	$68,000	$80,000	$91,950	1,347
OTA	Region	Northeast	$31,000	$38,953	$45,000	$54,107	$65,000	315
		South Atlantic	$34,450	$42,000	$50,000	$59,000	$66,900	273
		South Central	$38,050	$44,200	$50,000	$60,000	$72,000	237
		North Central	$30,000	$38,000	$44,000	$52,000	$60,000	630
		Mountain	$38,000	$40,000	$47,000	$55,750	$65,900	122
		Pacific	$35,000	$45,000	$52,000	$60,830	$74,700	130
	Work Setting Location	Urban	$35,000	$40,000	$48,000	$56,000	$67,000	640
		Suburban	$33,000	$40,000	$47,000	$56,000	$65,000	670
		Rural	$30,000	$37,732	$45,000	$52,979	$63,900	397

Table 3.7. Annual Salary Overview by Highest Degree Held in Occupational Therapy

		10th Percentile	25th Percentile	50th Percentile (Median)	75th Percentile	90th Percentile	Number of Responses
OT	Associate's Degree	$60,200	$66,000	$78,000	$92,250	$104,200	6
	Baccalaureate Degree	$50,000	$62,000	$75,000	$89,000	$100,980	2,463
	Certificate, None, Other	$50,000	$60,000	$75,000	$87,000	$110,000	145
	Master's Degree	$45,641	$56,000	$75,000	$76,000	$88,000	4,955
	PhD	$64,000	$76,500	$84,500	$100,000	$26,800	94
	Professional Doctorate Degree	$51,000	$60,000	$73,000	$84,000	$99,000	415
	ScD	$66,248	$75,000	$85,000	$90,000	$111,000	9
OTA	Associate's Degree	$25,000	$37,000	$46,000	$55,000	$65,000	1,578
	Baccalaureate Degree	$35,300	$40,000	$49,500	$59,250	$69, 200	36
	Certificate, None, Other	$22,000	$37,250	$47,000	$58,000	$69,700	81
	Master's Degree	$28,000	$39,750	$56,500	$77,500	$125,500	11
	Professional Doctorate Degree	—	—	—	—	—	1

Note: — = insufficient data for tabulation.

Table 3.8. Annual Salary Overview by AOTA Membership Status

		10th Percentile	25th Percentile	50th Percentile (Median)	75th Percentile	90th Percentile	Number of Responses
OT	Member	$48,000	$59,070	**$70,000**	$83,000	$96,000	5,006
	Former Member	$45,000	$56,000	**$67,000**	$78,000	$90,000	2,850
	Nonmember	$48,000	$56,000	**$66,500**	$78,000	$90,000	231
OTA	Member	$26,000	$38,000	**$49,500**	$56,000	$66,000	784
	Former Member	$26,000	$36,000	**$47,000**	$54,000	$64,900	754
	Nonmember	$29,000	$37,625	**$50,000**	$55,000	$60,000	169

Table 3.9. Annual Salary Overview by State

	OT						OTA	
	10th Percentile	25th Percentile	50th Percentile (Median)	75th Percentile	90th Percentile	Number of Responses	**Median**	Number of Responses
Alabama	$50,000	$60,000	**$67,000**	$84,000	$96,000	74	**$44,000**	13
Alaska	$56,000	$62,000	**$75,000**	$80,000	$87,000	27	**$41,341**	4
Arizona	$52,000	$62,000	**$71,000**	$90,000	$105,900	131	**$53,000**	29
Arkansas	$47,542	$58,000	**$66,580**	$80,000	$91,800	81	**$57,000**	23
California	$60,000	$70,000	**$80,000**	$91,640	$103,900	628	**$57,500**	74
Colorado	$48,100	$54,250	**$60,115**	$75,000	$83,000	176	**$44,000**	28
Connecticut	$60,000	$65,000	**$74,000**	$86,000	$94,900	122	**$45,000**	31
Delaware	$60,500	$70,500	**$77,000**	$89,750	$109,200	31	**$45,396**	4
District of Columbia	$60,200	$68,000	**$78,120**	$90,000	$100,000	56	—	1
Florida	$55,000	$62,000	**$74,000**	$83,540	$94,000	318	**$51,000**	83
Georgia	$52,000	$61,250	**$70,000**	$85,000	$96,000	158	**$53,760**	26
Hawaii	$58,200	$64,250	**$71,000**	$85,000	$89,750	29	—	3
Idaho	$45,300	$55,000	**$64,000**	$75,000	$85,799	48	**$54,000**	4
Illinois	$53,000	$60,000	**$67,800**	$80,000	$93,000	394	**$46,000**	78
Indiana	$49,000	$58,500	**$65,416**	$78,000	$92,410	214	**$43,500**	57
Iowa	$51,000	$55,250	**$66,000**	$75,750	$81,800	88	**$42,000**	19
Kansas	$50,200	$59,000	**$69,080**	$79,000	$85,000	74	**$41,000**	31
Kentucky	$50,500	$57,000	**$65,000**	$79,529	$85,000	116	**$43,500**	18
Louisiana	$56,200	$63,000	**$71,000**	$79,000	$90,000	86	**$46,500**	14
Maine	$38,200	$45,500	**$58,000**	$70,000	$77,800	95	**$42,500**	4
Maryland	$57,000	$62,500	**$72,000**	$85,750	$96,000	220	**$55,000**	33
Massachusetts	$50,000	$58,250	**$68,000**	$79,000	$92,000	316	**$45,000**	57
Michigan	$49,000	$55,000	**$63,000**	$75,000	$85,000	274	**$42,000**	48
Minnesota	$46,031	$53,000	**$62,700**	$73,000	$84,900	196	**$39,000**	38

(Continued)

Table 3.9. Annual Salary Overview by State *(cont.)*

	OT						OTA	
	10th Percentile	25th Percentile	**50th Percentile (Median)**	75th Percentile	90th Percentile	Number of Responses	**Median**	Number of Responses
Mississippi	$55,000	$62,000	**$69,000**	$83,862	$90,000	62	**$49,000**	11
Missouri	$45,300	$52,000	**$61,075**	$72,000	$85,900	160	**$40,000**	48
Montana	$40,200	$54,500	**$61,000**	$68,750	$88,072	25	**$44,560**	8
Nebraska	$55,050	$58,000	**$63,000**	$80,000	$94,800	66	**$43,200**	11
Nevada	$40,115	$65,000	**$75,000**	$90,000	$107,800	41	**$50,000**	10
New Hampshire	$43,350	$50,500	**$60,350**	$69,073	$75,600	49	**$43,000**	10
New Jersey	$59,100	$65,000	**$72,000**	$85,750	$95,968	253	**$56,000**	27
New Mexico	$52,100	$64,000	**$72,000**	$85,000	$93,600	67	**$50,250**	17
New York	$50,000	$58,000	**$67,000**	$79,000	$90,000	543	**$44,500**	82
North Carolina	$45,000	$54,000	**$61,000**	$76,000	$87,350	286	**$45,000**	59
North Dakota	$39,500	$50,000	**$53,500**	$66,500	$92,440	28	**$35,000**	3
Ohio	$52,000	$60,000	**$68,000**	$80,000	$91,980	533	**$45,000**	234
Oklahoma	$51,100	$59,813	**$70,000**	$78,000	$87,700	53	**$46,467**	30
Oregon	$50,000	$57,250	**$65,000**	$76,750	$89,528	101	**$47,500**	6
Pennsylvania	$52,100	$60,000	**$69,000**	$80,000	$89,000	398	**$43,000**	88
Puerto Rico	$23,900	$36,450	**$43,500**	$49,500	$81,300	10	**—**	1
Rhode Island	$48,550	$59,250	**$65,000**	$71,750	$76,599	35	**$40,000**	11
South Carolina	$55,100	$60,250	**$68,000**	$79,500	$89,900	84	**$50,000**	21
South Dakota	$52,100	$57,000	**$64,250**	$74,750	$104,550	21	**$37,643**	5
Tennessee	$50,000	$60,000	**$72,000**	$85,000	$100,000	136	**$46,526**	40
Texas	$56,000	$63,000	**$71,700**	$87,750	$100,000	448	**$55,000**	88
Utah	$42,300	$60,000	**$65,000**	$75,750	$86,700	54	**$46,000**	15
Vermont	$54,200	$61,500	**$72,000**	$79,000	$85,000	20	**$68,000**	5
Virginia	$55,000	$62,000	**$71,010**	$83,000	$95,000	216	**$55,000**	32
Washington	$48,100	$58,605	**$68,000**	$85,000	$97,630	219	**$48,500**	43
West Virginia	$50,000	$56,000	**$66,000**	$73,000	$87,200	38	**$47,000**	13
Wisconsin	$40,100	$52,000	**$59,000**	$73,000	$88,900	180	**$40,000**	44
Wyoming	$42,500	$56,000	**$64,950**	$69,750	$79,500	22	**$42,000**	11

Note: — = insufficient data for tabulation.

Table 3.10. Annual Salary Overview by Work Setting

		10th Percentile	25th Percentile	50th Percentile (Median)	75th Percentile	90th Percentile	Number of Responses
OT	Academia	$56,000	$65,000	**$77,000**	$90,000	$106,800	565
	Community	$46,100	$60,000	**$70,000**	$83,000	$95,000	149
	Early Intervention	$41,000	$50,000	**$60,000**	$72,000	$85,000	291
	Freestanding Outpatient	$47,100	$56,000	**$65,000**	$78,000	$93,000	810
	Home Health	$50,000	$62,100	**$76,000**	$90,000	$102,000	478
	Hospital (Non–Mental Health)	$51,230	$60,000	**$68,000**	$80,000	$93,000	2,225
	LTC/SNF	$50,000	$63,000	**$73,000**	$84,000	$94,960	1,624
	Mental Health	$49,000	$59,000	**$69,000**	$80,000	$91,900	206
	Schools	$43,000	$51,000	**$61,600**	$73,000	$85,000	1,605
	Other	$54,100	$60,000	**$71,000**	$87,360	$110,000	134
OTA	Academia	$50,000	$52,250	**$61,500**	$70,000	$89,700	26
	Community	$35,500	$43,250	**$49,000**	$55,000	$71,600	28
	Early Intervention	$14,100	$31,500	**$39,500**	$45,000	$56,800	38
	Freestanding Outpatient	$26,040	$36,000	**$43,100**	$52,000	$59,700	76
	Home Health	$29,100	$40,000	**$50,000**	$60,000	$74,800	60
	Hospital (Non–Mental Health)	$20,300	$36,250	**$43,000**	$50,750	$57,000	192
	LTC/SNF	$27,100	$40,000	**$50,000**	$58,000	$67,180	1,008
	Mental Health	$17,302	$36,250	**$45,000**	$50,750	$54,700	23
	Schools	$22,000	$30,000	**$36,000**	$45,000	$54,946	242
	Other	$28,050	$36,250	**$38,500**	$49,500	$57,500	14

Note: Data are limited to base annual salary received at the primary setting for individuals employed full-time.

Compensation Trends

Median compensation for an OT working full-time has increased 8.2% since the 2010 survey. This annual increase of 1.6% over the past 5 years is a much slower rate than what was seen during the 2006–2010 time period. Over the 14 years since the 2000 survey, full-time OTs have seen average annual increases of 4%. Part-time, both standard and limited, OTs saw very robust increases over the past 4 years, with increases of 29.4% and 24.3%, respectively. OTAs have seen slightly higher increases, up 9.1% since 2010 and 6% per year since 2000 (Table 3.11).

Trend data are provided for full-time OTs and OTAs according to primary work setting (Table 3.12) and region (Table 3.13). For OTs, the strongest percentage gains are seen in those working in the Home Health and Academia settings. Regionally, the strongest gains are seen among OTs in the Mountain region.

Compensation Differences by Gender

Previous studies have not delved into compensation differences by gender. This survey provided a large enough sample size to explore the issue on a macro level. Table 3.14 reflects the differences in salaried OTs and OTAs based on their gender. Overall, male OTs' median salary is $78,000, or 14.7% higher than the median salary of female OTs.

The sample size does not allow for further investigation but can provide some qualitative insight. Based on practice setting, the largest gap appears in Home Health, whereas differences appeared to be almost nonexistent in Community settings. Other settings reflect the overall trend.

Table 3.11. Compensation Trends, 2000–2014

		2014	2010	2006	2000	Percentage of Change, 2010–2014
OT	Full-Time	**$70,000**	$64,722	$55,800	$45,000	8.2%
	Standard Part-Time	**$44.00**	$34.00	$28.85	$18.69	29.4%
	Limited Part-Time	**$45.00**	$37.00	$25.64	$21.15	24.3%
OTA	Full-Time	**$48,000**	$44,000	$38,000	$30,000	9.1%
	Standard Part-Time	**$28.00**	$22.60	$16.75	$25.64	23.9%
	Limited Part-Time	**$30.00**	$24.23	$18.03	$36.06	23.8%

Note: Data are the median base annual salary or hourly rate for the primary setting.

Table 3.12. Annual Salary Trends by Work Setting, 2000–2014

		2014	2010	2006	2000	Percentage of Change, 2010–2014
OT	Academia	**$77,000**	$70,060	$66,000	$53,000	9.9%
	Community	**$67,000**	$68,000	$58,250	$43,062	−1.5%
	Early Intervention	**$60,000**	$59,850	*(included with Schools)*		0.3%
	Freestanding Outpatient	**$65,000**	$64,000	$57,000	$50,000	1.6%
	Home Health	**$76,000**	$68,000	$55,000	$45,000	11.8%
	Hospital (Non–Mental Health)	**$68,000**	$64,480	$58,000	$46,000	5.5%
	LTC/SNF	**$73,000**	$70,000	$58,000	$46,000	4.3%
	Mental Health	**$69,000**	$65,000	$53,750	$45,000	6.2%
	Schools	**$61,000**	$58,201	$50,500	$42,000	4.8%
	Other	**$70,000**	$67,122	$62,000	N/A	4.3%
OTA	Academia	**$61,500**	$52,000	$46,000	$37,000	18.3%
	Community	**$49,000**	$44,000	$35,000	—	11.3%
	Early Intervention	**$39,500**	$35,000	*(included with Schools)*		12.9%
	Freestanding Outpatient	**$43,200**	$41,800	$32,000	$30,000	3.3%
	Home Health	**$50,000**	$52,000	$45,000	$40,000	−3.8%
	Hospital (Non–Mental Health)	**$43,000**	$42,000	$41,000	$31,053	2.3%
	LTC/SNF	**$50,000**	$48,942	$40,000	$30,000	2.2%
	Mental Health	**$45,000**	$43,500	$39,000	$24,500	3.4%
	Schools	**$36,000**	$34,000	$31,075	$27,500	5.9%
	Other	**$39,000**	$41,592	$41,500	—	-6.2%

Note: All data are median annual base salary for full-time employees. — = insufficient data for tabulation.

Table 3.13. Annual Salary Trends by Region, 2000–2014

		2014	2010	2006	2000	Percentage of Change, 2010–2014
OT	**Region**					
	Northeast	**$68,000**	$64,000	$55,000	$46,000	6.3%
	South Atlantic	**$70,000**	$66,000	$58,558	$46,000	6.1%
	South Central	**$70,000**	$66,000	$60,000	$48,000	6.1%
	North Central	**$65,000**	$60,497	$53,000	$42,000	7.4%
	Mountain	**$66,000**	$61,000	$50,000	$44,000	8.2%
	Pacific	**$75,000**	$70,000	$60,076	$49,500	7.1%
	Work Setting Location					
	Urban	**$69,000**	$65,000	$58,000	$47,000	6.2%
	Suburban	**$68,000**	$65,000	$55,000	$45,000	4.6%
	Rural	**$68,000**	$62,000	$54,000	$44,000	9.7%
OTA	**Region**					
	Northeast	**$45,000**	$41,000	$35,500	$30,500	9.7%
	South Atlantic	**$50,000**	$48,000	$42,000	$30,000	4.1%
	South Central	**$50,000**	$49,764	$40,000	$30,500	0.5%
	North Central	**$43,000**	$41,350	$39,000	$27,000	4.0%
	Mountain	**$47,000**	$43,000	$28,595	$30,000	9.3%
	Pacific	**$50,000**	$48,000	$40,000	$29,000	4.1%
	Work Setting Location					
	Urban	**$47,500**	$45,730	$40,000	$30,000	3.9%
	Suburban	**$46,446**	$43,680	$39,548	$30,000	6.3%
	Rural	**$45,000**	$42,000	$35,000	$31,645	7.1%

Note: All data are median annual base salary for full-time employees.

Table 3.14. Full-Time Compensation by Gender

		10th Percentile	25th Percentile	**50th Percentile (Median)**	75th Percentile	90th Percentile	Number of Responses
OT	Female	$50,000	$58,000	**$68,000**	$80,000	$93,000	6,994
	Male	$58,000	$67,000	**$78,000**	$90,000	$105,000	754
OTA	Female	$32,000	$40,000	**$48,000**	$56,000	$65,000	1,357
	Male	$38,000	$43,000	**$50,000**	$57,000	$75,000	161

Additional Compensation

In addition to base salary information, the respondents were asked to indicate whether they received any type of additional cash compensation in 2014 from their primary setting, such as a bonus, stipend, or any other cash-based payment. As summarized in Figure 3.1, 25.7% of the respondents indicated receiving such payments, down from 29.9% in 2010. 27.4% of OTs responded affirmatively, whereas 18% of OTAs indicated they had received additional compensation.

Respondents who received a bonus reported receiving a median of $1,000, down from $1,500 in 2010. However, the median is $1,200 for full-time OTs and $500 for full-time OTAs (Table 3.15).

Responses vary strongly, as expected, based on the work hour classification—27.9% of full-time employees received additional cash compensation vs. less than 15% of the limited part-time employees. Almost 30% of full-time OTs received a bonus as compared with 19.6% of full-time OTAs. Segmenting responses further shows, among other things, that those in the Academia setting received the largest amount (median of $3,800; Table 3.16).

Additional Work Settings

As noted in Module 2, nearly one-third of the respondents reported that they work in more than one work setting. Those who are employed in multiple settings reported working at their non-primary setting for a median of 6 hours per week, which generated a median of $6,000 in income for 2014 (Table 3.17).

Figure 3.1. Additional compensation.

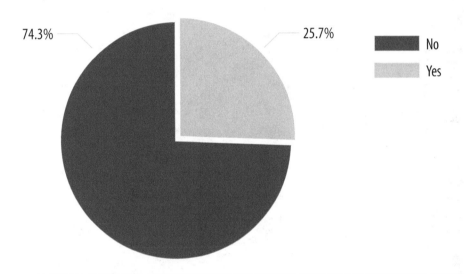

74.3%   25.7%

- No
- Yes

Table 3.15. Value of Additional Cash Compensation

	10th Percentile	25th Percentile	50th Percentile (Median)	75th Percentile	90th Percentile	Number of Responses
Overall	$200	$500	**$1,000**	$3,000	$7,000	3,036
OT	$200	$500	**$1,200**	$3,000	$7,500	2,656
OTA	$100	$300	**$500**	$1,500	$4,000	380

Note: Data include respondents who are full- and part-time workers.

Table 3.16. Additional Cash Compensation

		Received Additional Cash Compensation	Median Amount Received
OT/OTA Status	OT	27.4%	$1,200
	OTA	18.0%	$500
Work Setting	Academia	38.7%	$3,800
	Community	21.2%	$1,900

(Continued)

Table 3.16. Additional Cash Compensation *(cont.)*

		Received Additional Cash Compensation	Median Amount Received
Work Setting	Early Intervention	25.5%	$1,000
	Freestanding Outpatient	35.0%	$1,000
	Home Health	25.5%	$1,500
	Hospital (Non–Mental Health)	29.7%	$1,000
	LTC/SNF	18.5%	$1,000
	Mental Health	18.0%	$800
	Schools	23.9%	$1,000
	Other	23.6%	$1,000
Total Years of Experience	0–1	17.9%	$1,000
	1.1–2	25.6%	$1,000
	2.1–4	26.7%	$1,000
	4.1–6	28.0%	$957
	6.1–9	25.0%	$1,000
	9.1–14	24.8%	$1,000
	14.1–20	26.6%	$1,050
	20.1–25	27.2%	$1,700
	25+	27.7%	$1,500
Years in Current Position	0–1	24.1%	$1,800
	1.1–2	29.6%	$1,200
	2.1–4	27.3%	$1,000
	4.1–6	28.2%	$1,000
	6.1–9	25.9%	$1,000
	9.1–15	25.2%	$1,000
	15+	28.8%	$1,500

Table 3.17. Income From Additional Work Settings

		Worked in Additional Settings	Median Hours Worked Per Week in Additional Settings	Median Income Received
	Overall	**28.3%**	**6**	**$6,000**
OT/OTA Status	OT	28.7%	6	$6,500
	OTA	26.5%	7	$5,000
Years of Professional Experience	0–5	27.6%	6	$5,000
	5.1–10	31.6%	6	$6,000
	10.1–15	28.4%	6	$6,400
	15.1–25	27.2%	6	$7,200
	25+	27.3%	6	$6,750

Module 4.
Benefits

Overview

This module explores baseline benefits received by the respondents. Only basic benefits are examined, such as health insurance, state licensure fees, pension plans, and similar benefits that are typically considered "standard" in many work environments.

Exploring benefits can be as complex as exploring compensation, with many detailed nuances based on the work setting and situation. However, to keep the survey length manageable, the goal of the benefits section was to provide a basic overview. As such, details such as the amount the employer pays for employees' health insurance premiums or the number of days received as paid time off were not collected. The respondents were asked only to indicate which benefits they receive and whether they were through their primary or secondary work setting (or both). (Additional breakouts for benefits are provided in Modules 7–16 for each specific work setting.)

Benefits Received

Paid time off (vacation or sick leave) is the benefit received most often by survey respondents, cited by nearly 80% as a benefit received. In addition, a majority of the respondents receive health insurance, dental insurance, continuing education and conference fees, life insurance, an employee-funded retirement plan, and disability insurance.

Most of these benefits are received through the primary work setting. Health and dental insurance are the most common benefits received through a secondary work setting, but each are cited by roughly 5%. Overall responses are summarized in Table 4.1.

The prevalence of receiving benefits has increased since 2010 for every benefit tracked except for continuing education, company-paid pension plans, college-level tuition reimbursement, or fees for advanced practice certification. As summarized in Table 4.2, the changes are modest at best, with no appreciable shift in the relative amount of any of the benefits (e.g., the most commonly received benefits in 2010 are also the most common in 2014).

Table 4.1. Benefits Received

	Receive From Any Setting	Receive From Primary Setting	Receiving From Another Work Setting	No Benefits Received
Paid Time Off (Vacation or Sick Leave)	79.8%	78.1%	1.7%	20.2%
Health Insurance	73.8%	68.2%	5.6%	26.2%
Dental Insurance	68.7%	63.9%	4.8%	31.3%
Continuing Education/Conference Fees	60.2%	57.3%	2.9%	39.8%
Life Insurance	61.0%	56.4%	4.6%	39.0%
Employee-Funded Retirement Plan (e.g., 401K)	62.6%	59.4%	3.2%	37.4%
Disability Insurance (Short- or Long-Term)	51.2%	53.8%	2.6%	43.6%
Professional Liability Insurance	45.8%	41.4%	4.4%	54.2%
Company-Paid Traditional Pension Plan	23.6%	21.5%	2.1%	76.4%
State Licensure Fees	20.9%	17.5%	3.4%	79.1%
AOTA Membership Fees	16.9%	13.9%	3.0%	83.1%
College-Level Tuition Reimbursement or Fees for Advanced Practice Certification	14.0%	11.7%	2.3%	86.0%

Table 4.2. Benefits Trends

	2014	2010
Paid Time Off (Vacation or Sick Leave)	78.1%	77.2%
Health Insurance	68.2%	69.7%
Dental Insurance	63.9%	63.8%
Continuing Education/Conference Fees	57.3%	62.7%
Life Insurance	56.4%	58.8%
Employee-Funded Retirement Plan (e.g., 401K)	59.4%	58.1%
Disability Insurance (Short- or Long-Term)	51.2%	51.6%
Professional Liability Insurance	41.4%	43.1%
Company-Paid Traditional Pension Plan	21.5%	27.4%
State Licensure Fees	17.5%	18.4%
AOTA Membership Fees	13.9%	15.7%
College-Level Tuition Reimbursement or Fees for Advanced Practice Certification	11.7%	14.0%

Note: Data are based on primary work setting benefits.

Module 5.
Workforce Dynamics

Overview

This module explores a variety of issues related to the dynamics affecting the occupational therapy workforce. These issues include job mobility (e.g., how often practitioners change jobs), reasons for job changes, unemployment rates in the profession for 2014, and the perceptions of those who are looking to leave the occupational therapy profession.

Note that many of the tables in this section are based on a far smaller number of respondents because of the question structure (e.g., only those who have changed jobs in the past 2 years were asked to describe the reasons why).

Job Mobility

Job turnover rates continue to decline, reaching their lowest level to date. As summarized in Table 5.1, 20.7% of the OTs reported that they changed jobs in the past 2 years. This number represents a small decrease from the 21.7% who reported changing jobs in the 2010 survey and a nearly 6% drop from 2006. For further context, the highest recorded turnover rate was 33.6% in 1997. As in all past studies, respondents who changed jobs typically did so only once in the past 2 years, with a few changing jobs 3 or more times.

Historically OTAs have had more job mobility than OTs; however, in this survey, the gap has closed substantially. Perhaps the most pronounced change in mobility is the increase in the number of OTAs who stated they have not changed jobs in the past 2 years. Only 22.5%, vs. 28.1% in 2010, of OTAs changed jobs in the past 2 years. This difference denotes a 19.8% decrease in mobility over the past 4 years and a remarkable 33% decrease from 2000.

Examining job mobility by primary work setting shows that the most active job changers are employed in the Home Health setting. Those least likely to have changed jobs are employed in the Hospital (Non–Mental Health) and Academia settings. In addition, as expected, job mobility decreases markedly as years of experience increase. Responses for various categories are provided in Table 5.2.

The opportunity to work in a more desirable or flexible employment setting continues to lead the list of reasons for changing jobs, cited by 40.7%. Although still a small percentage of the total, "reduction in hours or salary" grew from 5.8% in 2010 to 9% in this survey. Other major factors for changing jobs are enhanced salary or benefits, family or personal reasons, and the opportunity to work with a different client population (Table 5.3).

Only minor differences exist in the reasons for changing jobs between OTs and OTAs. The main reasons for both groups are opportunity to work in a more desirable or flexible setting, better salary or benefits, and family or personal reasons (Table 5.4).

Table 5.1. Job Mobility Trends

	OT					OTA				
	2014	2010	2006	2000	1997	**2014**	2010	2006	2000	1997
Never Changed Jobs in the Past 2 Years	**79.3%**	78.4%	73.2%	71.2%	66.4%	**77.5%**	71.9%	74.2%	66%	67.3%
Changed Jobs Once	**1.4%**	16.8%	20.2%	20.1%	24.2%	**18.5%**	21.3%	17.6%	22.4%	23.3%
Changed Jobs Twice	**2.3%**	3.5%	4.1%	5.6%	6.8%	**2.9%**	4.5%	5.7%	7.9%	7.1%
Changed Jobs 3 or More Times	**1.0%**	1.4%	2.4%	3.1%	2.6%	**1.1%**	2.3%	2.5%	3.7%	2.3%

Table 5.2. Job Mobility

		Never Changed Jobs in Past 2 Years	Changed Jobs Once	Changed Jobs Twice	Changed Jobs 3 or More Times
	Overall	**79.0%**	**17.6%**	**2.4%**	**1.0%**
Number of Hours Worked Per Week at Primary Work Setting	1–10	72.0%	22.9%	3.5%	1.6%
	11–29	75.5%	20.6%	3.0%	0.9%
	30+	79.8%	16.9%	2.3%	1.0%
Primary Work Setting	Academia	82.5%	16.2%	1.1%	0.2%
	Community	77.4%	18.6%	3.1%	0.9%
	Early Intervention	78.4%	17.8%	2.8%	1.0%
	Freestanding Outpatient	77.0%	19.7%	2.7%	0.6%
	Home Health	69.4%	24.3%	5.1%	1.2%
	Hospital (Non–Mental Health)	83.6%	14.4%	1.5%	0.5%
	LTC/SNF	73.9%	20.7%	3.4%	1.9%
	Mental Health	80.4%	17.6%	0.8%	0.8%
	Schools	83.1%	14.5%	1.7%	0.7%
	Other	81.9%	14.8%	1.1%	2.2%
Years of Professional Experience	0–5	70.8%	24.1%	3.5%	1.6%
	5.1–10	77.2%	19.2%	2.6%	1.0%
	10.1–15	84.4%	13.4%	2.0%	0.4%
	15.1–25	84.7%	12.6%	2.0%	0.7%
	25+	89.5%	9.2%	1.0%	0.4%
AOTA Membership	Member	79.6%	17.3%	2.3%	0.8%
	Former Member	77.7%	18.2%	2.7%	1.4%
	Nonmember	80.4%	16.2%	1.8%	1.6%

Note: Percentages do not add to 100 due to rounding.

Table 5.3. Reasons for Changing Jobs

	2014	2010	2006	2000
Opportunity to Work in a More Desirable/Flexible Employment Setting	40.7%	42.8%	46.9%	51.2%
Better Salary/Benefits at New Job	27.2%	31.7%	29.8%	24.3%
Family/Personal Reasons	24.2%	27.2%	—	—
Better Hours at New Job	19.8%	18.2%	21.0%	—
Opportunity to Work With a Different Client Population	19.3%	21.2%	25.3%	27.2%
Opportunity for Greater Responsibility/Advancement	16.7%	16.1%	18.0%	20.1%
Productivity Requirements Were Too High	11.6%	11.5%	9.6%	—
Downsizing/Elimination of Position at Previous Place of Employment	6.9%	6.7%	5.9%	27.2%
Reduction in Hours or Salary at Previous Place of Employment	9.0%	5.8%	4.0%	27.0%
Relocation of Self or Spouse	5.7%	6.4%	—	—
Wanted to Start Own Practice/Work as a Contractor/Per Diem	3.2%	3.9%	5.6%	8.4%
Employer Shut Down/Agency Lost Contract	0.3%	1.1%	—	—
Fired	0.9%	0.9%	0.9%	1.8%
Other	20.4%	18.5%	31.6%	19.7%

Note: Data include only respondents who changed jobs in the past 2 years. "Other" includes personal issues such as a desire for a shorter commute, general dissatisfaction with employer, start or return to school, and similar situations. — = choice not offered in the survey.

Table 5.4. Reasons for Changing Jobs According to Practitioner Status

	Overall	OT	OTA
Opportunity to Work in a More Desirable/Flexible Employment Setting	40.7%	41.8%	36.0%
Better Salary/Benefits at New Job	27.2%	26.8%	29.3%
Family/Personal Reasons	24.2%	25.6%	18.4%
Opportunity to Work With a Different Client Population	19.3%	20.5%	14.6%
Better Hours at New Job	19.8%	19.8%	19.9%
Opportunity for Greater Responsibility/Advancement	16.7%	18.6%	9.8%
Productivity Requirements Were Too High	11.6%	12.0%	10.0%
Downsizing/Elimination of Position at Previous Place of Employment	6.9%	6.1%	10.6%
Relocation of Self or Spouse	5.7%	6.2%	3.8%
Reduction in Hours or Salary at Previous Place of Employment	9.0%	7.9%	13.4%
Wanted to Start Own Practice/Work as a Contractor/Per Diem	3.2%	3.8%	4.2%
Fired	0.9%	0.7%	1.7%
Other	18.5%	22.7%	24.9%

Note: Data include only the 2,183 respondents who changed jobs in the past 2 years.

Unemployment Trends

Although the number of respondents who said they were unemployed remained low, there was a measurable increase in the percentage and duration of time respondents were unemployed. Overall, those who said they were unemployed for any period of time in the past 12 months grew from 7.5% in 2010 to 10.4% in 2014, a 38.7% increase. OTAs were more likely to have been out of work, with 15.2% unemployed in 2014. In addition, the median length of unemployment for OTAs returned to 2006 levels, increasing by 2 weeks from 10 weeks in 2010 to 12 weeks in 2014 (Table 5.5).

Leaving the Occupational Therapy Profession

Little change has occurred in the percentage of respondents who are planning on or considering leaving the occupational therapy profession in the next 2 years (by 2016). Only 9.2% of the respondents are considering or planning to leave the profession, compared with 7.8% in 2010 (Table 5.6). This metric hit its peak in 2000, with 18.2% responding that they were considering leaving the field.

A higher percentage of respondents with 25 or more years of professional experience are strongly considering or planning on leaving the profession compared with other respondents with less experience. This finding is expected because this group is likely thinking about retirement. Higher percentages for planning on or considering leaving are also seen for those working part-time. Small differences are seen based on work setting, with respondents working in the Home Health, Community, LTC/SNF, and Mental Health setting most likely to be at least considering leaving the profession by 2016.

No single reason dominated the responses of respondents planning on or considering leaving the profession. "Other" was by far the most cited reason for considering leaving the field. Burnout, physical demands, lack of advancement, and reduction in paid hours were all common themes. "Dissatisfaction with the occupational therapy profession" was the next most common response, and the 2014 percentage for this reason was very close to the 2010 percentage, when it was added to the survey for the first time. Responses are summarized in Table 5.7.

Table 5.5. Unemployment Trends, 2009–2014

		Unemployed Any Time in 2014	Median Weeks Unemployed	Unemployed Any Time in 2009	Median Weeks Unemployed
	Overall	**10.4%**	**12**	**7.5%**	**10.0**
OT/OTA Status	OT	9.3%	12	7.0%	10.0
	OTA	15.2%	12	10.8%	12.0
Primary Work Setting	Academia	3.2%	8	2.5%	8.0
	Community	8.0%	12	6.3%	13.5
	Early Intervention	11.2%	12	5.9%	10.0
	Freestanding Outpatient	11.5%	12	7.6%	8.5
	Home Health	9.7%	12	7.3%	12.0
	Hospital (Non–Mental Health)	7.7%	10	6.6%	12.0
	LTC/SNF	14.3%	12	10.2%	8.0
	Mental Health	7.7%	10	3.6%	10.5
	Schools	10.9%	10	8.5%	10.0
	Other	8.8%	12	5.0%	20.0

Table 5.6. Future Plans

Note: Percentages do not add to 100 due to rounding.

		Will Leave the Field	Strongly Considering Leaving	Somewhat Considering Leaving	No Plans to Leave
	Overall 2000	1.4%	3.5%	13.3%	81.8%
	Overall 2006	2.0%	2.0%	8.6%	87.4%
	Overall 2010	0.6%	1.3%	5.9%	92.2%
	Overall 2014	**0.6%**	**1.5%**	**7.1%**	**90.9%**
OT/OTA Status	OT	0.5%	1.1%	5.3%	91.6%
	OTA	0.6%	1.9%	9.8%	87.7%
	0–5	0.3%	0.6%	5.2%	93.9%
	5.1–10	0.3%	1.5%	6.9%	91.4%
Years of Professional Experience	10.1–15	0.5%	1.7%	8.6%	89.3%
	15.1–25	0.6%	2.0%	8.7%	88.7%
	25+	1.8%	2.6%	8.6%	87.0%
Number of Hours Per Week at Primary Work Setting	1–10	0.8%	3.5%	10.0%	85.6%
	11–29	1.1%	1.9%	9.7%	87.4%
	30+	0.5%	1.3%	6.5%	91.7%
	Academia	1.4%	1.3%	5.3%	92.0%
	Community	0.4%	2.2%	9.3%	88.1%
	Early Intervention	0.2%	0.4%	5.2%	94.2%
	Freestanding Outpatient	0.4%	1.8%	4.3%	93.4%
Primary Work Setting	Home Health	0.3%	2.8%	9.8%	87.1%
	Hospital (Non–Mental Health)	0.3%	1.0%	5.7%	93.0%
	LTC/SNF	0.6%	1.8%	9.0%	88.6%
	Mental Health	1.2%	1.5%	8.4%	88.9%
	Schools	0.8%	1.2%	6.8%	91.3%
	Other	2.2%	1.1%	11.5%	85.2%
AOTA Membership Status	Member	0.6%	1.2%	6.5%	91.7%
	Former Member	0.5%	1.8%	7.8%	89.9%
	Nonmember	0.4%	2.0%	8.2%	89.4%

Table 5.7. Reasons for Leaving the Occupational Therapy Field

	Desire to Work in a Different Field	Planning to Temporarily Stop Working	Planning to Permanently Stop Working	Dissatisfied With the Profession	Other
Overall 2000	42.8%	15.2%	11.0%	—	39.7%
Overall 2006	49.3%	20.4%	15.4%	—	8.8%
Overall 2010	31.2%	12.4%	22.6%	21.8%	30.6%
Overall 2014	**19.2%**	**5.9%**	**14.9%**	**22.0%**	**38.2%**

Note: Responses include only practitioners who are planning on or considering leaving the profession in the near term. — = choice not offered in the survey. Percentages do not add to 100 due to rounding.

Module 6.
Students

Overview

This module is limited to the 1,273 respondents who identified themselves as either a full-time or part-time student in the occupational therapy field and not employed in the occupational therapy profession in 2014.

Because these respondents were not employed in the profession in 2014, they were not asked the in-depth questions concerning compensation, work situations, and other employment-related questions the practitioners were asked. The students were asked a different set of questions about demographics, future plans concerning advanced degrees, career path interests, and overall impression of the "health" of the occupational therapy job market.

Location

The students are mainly located in the Northeast and North Central regions, with these regions accounting for 56.4% of the respondents (Figure 6.1). The top 4 states represented in the sample are New York, California, Pennsylvania, and Texas, which collectively account for 29.8% of the sample.[1]

Figure 6.1. Geographic distribution of student respondents.

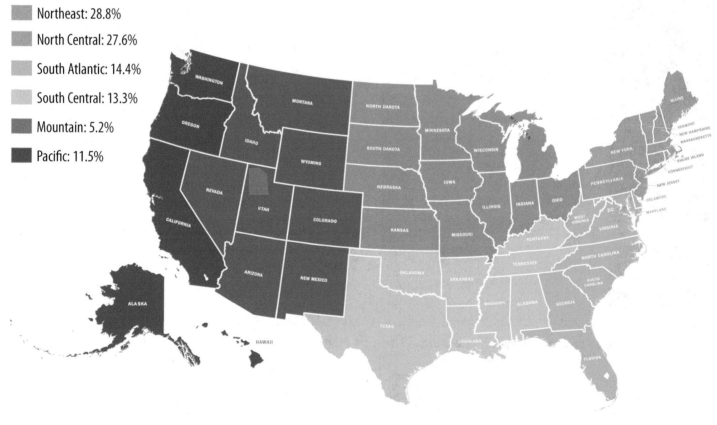

- Northeast: 28.8%
- North Central: 27.6%
- South Atlantic: 14.4%
- South Central: 13.3%
- Mountain: 5.2%
- Pacific: 11.5%

Note: Percentages do not add to 100 due to rounding.

[1] The survey question was phrased "In what state are you located?" to avoid the complexities of accounting for the geographic mobility that is typically seen in a student population. Thus, the location data may refer to the home or school location of the respondent.

AOTA Membership Status

A strong majority, 89.9% of the respondents, are current AOTA members. Most of the remaining are former members (7.2%), and 2.9% never joined AOTA (Figure 6.2).

Demographics Snapshot

Women comprise 86.5% of student respondents, and men as a group have grown from 2010's 6.7% to nearly 13% in this sample. The student demographics are analogous with those of the sample of all practitioners, with the most substantial difference being an increase in ethnic diversity among the student sample (Table 6.1).

Degrees Held and Pursuing

The students are primarily master's-level degree candidates. Still, as summarized in Table 6.2, the student sample encompasses a diverse number of degree pursuits, ranging from certificate to doctoral-level degrees.

The respondents were also asked to indicate their anticipated graduation year. 38.2% expect to graduate in 2015, and 27.5% expect to graduate in 2014 (Figure 6.3).

Interest in Doctoral-Level Degree

Students have a fairly strong interest in pursuing a doctoral-level degree. As summarized in Figure 6.4, in answer to the question "Looking a few years into the future, do you think you will pursue a doctorate-level degree?" about 2%

more state they will definitely pursue a doctoral degree as compared to 2010 survey respondents, and 4.6% fewer say pursuing one is a possibility.

Figure 6.2. Student AOTA membership status.

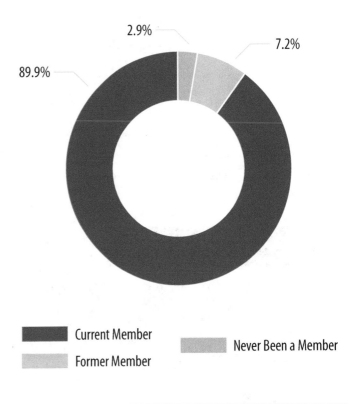

Table 6.1. Demographic Comparison

		Students	All Practitioners
	Overall	**1,273**	**11,779**
Gender	Female	86.5%	90.9%
	Male	12.9%	8.8%
	No Response	0.7%	0.3%
Ethnic Background	African-American/Black	4.6%	3.1%
	American Indian/Alaskan Native	0.7%	0.3%
	Asian/Pacific Islander	7.0%	4.4%
	Caucasian/White	77.1%	85.3%
	Hispanic/Latino	4.7%	3.2%
	Multiethnic	3.1%	1.4%
	No response	2.7%	2.2%

Note: Percentages do not add to 100 due to rounding.

Table 6.2. Educational Degrees

Note: Percentages do not add to 100 due to rounding.

	Students Pursuing	Practitioners Holding
Certificate	0.8%	1.0%
Associate's Degree	20.2%	16.8%
Baccalaureate Degree	2.3%	26.6%
Master's Degree	70.2%	49.6%
Professional Doctorate Degree	4.9%	3.9%
PhD	0.1%	0.9%
ScD	0.2%	0.1%
None	1.2%	0.6%
No Response	0.8%	0.8%

Figure 6.3. Anticipated graduation year.

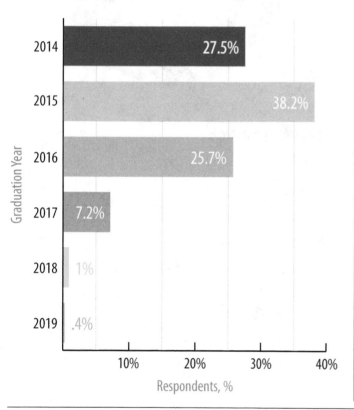

Figure 6.4. Interest in pursuing a doctoral-level degree.

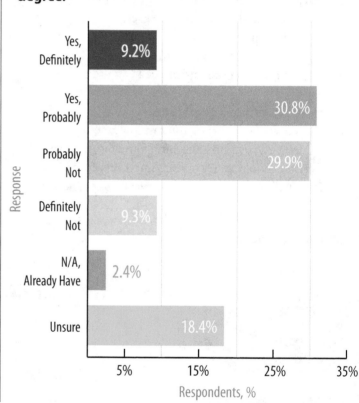

Future Plans

The respondents were asked to indicate whether they were considering a career in academia (Figure 6.5), a career as a researcher (Figure 6.6), or opening their own private practice (Figure 6.7). Each response gained interest since the 2010 survey. Opening up a private practice is the most appealing of the options, with well over half, 58.2% vs. 47.1% in 2010, saying they are either "strongly" or "somewhat" considering such a move. Although still a majority, 50.3% vs. 38.1% in 2010 feel the same way about a career in academia. A career as a researcher holds the least appeal of the three choices, with only 23.9%, vs. 21% in 2010, say-ing they are at least "somewhat" interested in this career direction.

State of the Job Market

The students are optimistic about the occupational ther-apy job market. When asked the question "Based on your experience, and what you have heard from others or have read, how 'healthy' do you feel the market is regarding job availability in the occupational therapy field?" most rated the market as healthy, with a majority selecting the top 3 points on a 0- to 10-point scale (Figure 6.8).

Figure 6.5. Future plans in academia.

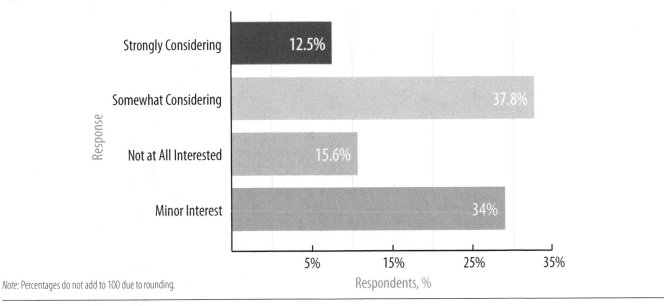

Note: Percentages do not add to 100 due to rounding.

Figure 6.6. Future plans as a researcher.

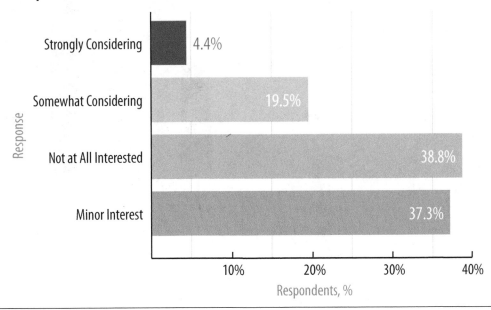

Figure 6.7. Future plans in private practice.

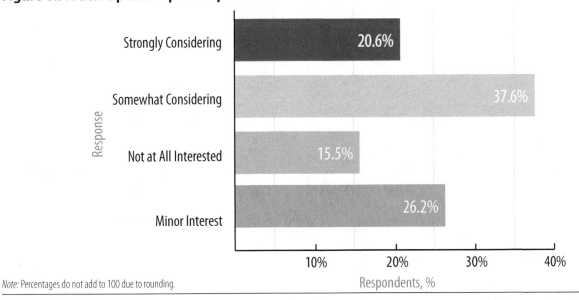

Note: Percentages do not add to 100 due to rounding.

Figure 6.8. Perceptions of the occupational therapy job market.

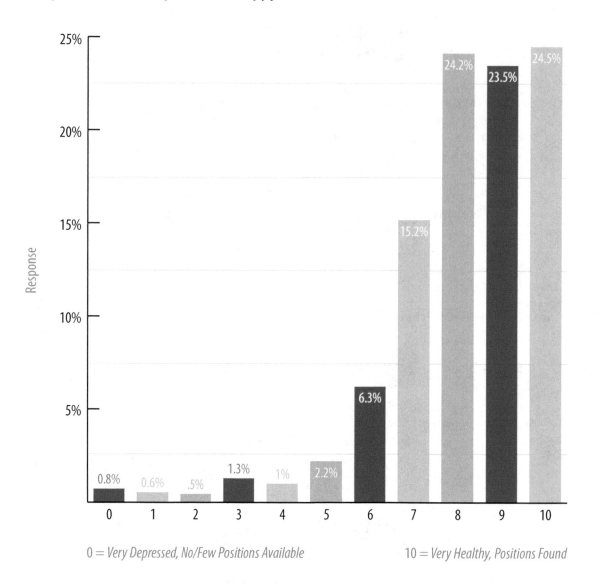

Note: Percentages do not add to 100 due to rounding.

Module 7.
Setting Focus: Academia

Table 7.1. Demographic Snapshot: Academia Setting

		Academia Setting	Full Sample
	Total Sample Size	**623**	**11,779**
	Median Age, Years	**52**	**39**
Gender	Female	88.6%	90.9%
	Male	11.4%	8.8%
OT/OTA Status	OT	95.2%	82.0%
	OTA	4.9%	18.0%
Highest Degree Held in Occupational Therapy	Certificate	1.1%	1.0%
	Associate's Degree	4.2%	16.8%
	Baccalaureate Degree	24.6%	26.6%
	Master's Degree	33.2%	49.4%
	Professional Doctorate Degree	18.9%	3.9%
	PhD	12.2%	0.9%
	ScD	0.8%	0.1%
	None/Other	5.0%	1.4%
Hold Advanced Certification/ Recognition	Currently Hold	29.8%	18.6%
	Pursuing	3.1%	5.2%
	Plan to Start	8.2%	18.2%
	No Plans to Start	59.1%	58.0%
Ethnic Background	African-American/Black	3.9%	3.1%
	American Indian/Alaskan Native	0.5%	0.3%
	Asian/Pacific Islander	4.3%	4.4%
	Caucasian/White	86.2%	85.3%
	Hispanic/Latino	2.1%	3.2%
	Multiethnic	1.1%	1.4%
	Prefer Not to Respond	1.9%	2.2%

(Continued)

Table 7.1. Demographic Snapshot: Academia Setting *(cont.)*

		Academia Setting	Full Sample
Total Years of Experience (Median)	Professional	18	9
	In Current Position at Current Setting	5	4
Region	Northeast	22.6%	22.0%
	South Atlantic	18.4%	17.0%
	South Central	16.4%	12.9%
	North Central	29.2%	29.0%
	Mountain	5.8%	7.3%
	Pacific	7.5%	11.9%
AOTA Membership Status	Member	97.1%	58.6%
	Former Member	2.4%	37.2%
	Nonmember	0.5%	4.2%

Note: Percentages do not add to 100 due to rounding as well as "Other" and "Prefer not to answer" responses.

Table 7.2. Position Profile: Academia Setting

Current Position	Dean	1.1%
	Chair	4.2%
	Program Director	16.2%
	Chair/Program Director	7.9%
	Faculty Member	46.8%
	Academic Fieldwork Coordinator	18.3%
	Other	5.6%
Rank	Full Professor	16.2%
	Associate Professor	22.9%
	Assistant Professor	31.9%
	Instructor	19.6%
	Other	9.5%
Institution Type	Private Institution	46.2%
	Public Institution	53.8%
Academic Responsibilities	Primarily for OT Program	72.3%
	Primarily for OTA Program	26.2%
	Other	1.5%

Note: Percentages do not add to 100 due to rounding.

Figure 7.1. Contract length.

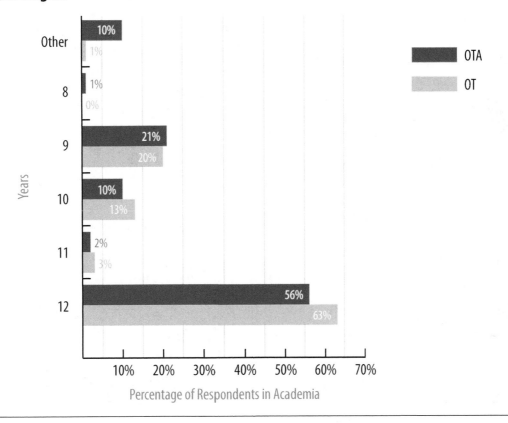

Percentage of Respondents in Academia

Table 7.3. Annual Compensation, 11- or 12-Month Contract, Full-Time Employment: Academia Setting

		Number of Responses	Median Compensation	Receiving Additional Cash Compensation	Median Additional Cash Compensation
	Overall	**378**	**$80,000**	**34%**	**$3,000**
OT/OTA Status	OT	362	$81,000	35%	$3,000
	OTA	16	$63,000	25%	$2,150
Years of Professional Experience	0–5	35	$70,000	31%	$4,600
	5.1–10	62	$75,000	35%	$2,000
	10.1–15	58	$77,000	38%	$3,000
	15.1–25	105	$81,000	36%	$4,000
	25+	118	$87,000	31%	$2,225
Years in Current Position at Present Setting	0–2	69	$74,000	29%	$2,500
	2.1–5	139	$76,000	37%	$3,000
	5.1–10	59	$80,000	27%	$2,750
	10+	111	$90,000	39%	$3,500

(Continued)

Table 7.3. Annual Compensation, 11- or 12-Month Contract, Full-Time Employment: Academia Setting *(cont.)*

		Number of Responses	Median Compensation	Receiving Additional Cash Compensation	Median Additional Cash Compensation
Highest Degree Held in Occupational Therapy	Associate's Degree	11	$59,000	27%	$1,800
	Baccalaureate Degree	106	$83,500	30%	$2,500
	Master's Degree	127	$76,500	34%	$3,000
	Professional Doctorate Degree	78	$79,000	60%	$4,000
	PhD	56	$89,000	52%	$3,000
Hold Advanced Practice Certification/ Recognition	Currently Hold	111	$82,000	30%	$3,000
	Do Not Hold	267	$80,000	36%	$3,000
Region	Northeast	69	$81,000	32%	$3,000
	South Atlantic	82	$80,000	35%	$2,500
	South Central	69	$80,000	33%	$2,000
	North Central	111	$79,000	38%	$4,250
	Mountain	26	$80,000	35%	$2,000
	Pacific	21	$90,000	24%	$5,000
Position	Chair	22	$111,500	50%	$6,000
	Program Director	77	$86,000	34%	$2,000
	Chair/Program Director	32	$96,000	41%	$5,500
	Faculty Member	148	$80,000	36%	$3,000
	Academic Fieldwork Coordinator	76	$72,000	25%	$2,500
	Other	23	$81,000	35%	$2,500
Rank	Full Professor	62	$104,500	35%	$5,000
	Associate Professor	96	$90,500	36%	$2,750
	Assistant Professor	116	$79,000	34%	$2,500
	Instructor	75	$65,000	33%	$2,500
	Other	29	$73,000	31%	$3,500
Academic Responsibilities	For OT Program	267	$84,000	38%	$3,000
	For OTA Program	92	$70,000	25%	$2,500
	Other	19	$76,000	26%	2,500
Institution Type	Public	187	$80,000	35%	$3,000
	Private	191	$81,000	34%	$3,000

Table 7.4. Annual Compensation, 9- or 10-Month Contract, Full-Time Employment: Academia Setting

		Number of Responses	Median Compensation	Receiving Additional Cash Compensation	Median Additional Cash Compensation
	Overall	**184**	**$69,000**	**51%**	**$5,000**
OT/OTA Status	OT	175	$70,000	52%	$5,000
	OTA	9	$58,000	22%	—
Years of Professional Experience	0–5	11	$58,500	45%	$4,000
	5.1–10	27	$65,000	37%	$5,000
	10.1–15	30	$64,250	30%	$10,000
	15.1–25	45	$67,000	60%	$4,750
	25+	71	$76,000	59%	$5,000
Years in Current Position at Present Setting	0–2	28	$63,000	32%	$5,000
	2.1–5	62	$63,500	52%	$4,100
	5.1–10	29	$66,000	45%	$5,000
	10+	65	$77,000	60%	$5,000
Highest Degree Held in the Occupational Therapy Field	Associate's Degree	9	$58,175	22%	—
	Baccalaureate Degree	42	$70,500	60%	$4,450
	Master's Degree	65	$65,000	43%	$5,000
	Professional Doctorate Degree	34	$70,000	17%	$5,000
	PhD	18	$76,500	39%	$5,000
	None/Other	16	$74,000	38%	$4,000
Advanced Practice Certification/Recognition	Currently Hold	57	$69,000	56%	$4,900
	Do Not Hold	127	$68,500	48%	$5,000
Region	Northeast	59	$70,000	61%	$5,000
	South Atlantic	22	$70,500	50%	$4,955
	South Central	22	$65,080	45%	$5,000
	North Central	54	$66,500	50%	$5,000
	Mountain	61	$69,000	2%	—
	Pacific	21	$69,040	38%	$4,500
Position	Chair	3	$98,000	67%	—
	Program Director	20	$74,500	70%	$6,000
	Chair/Program Director	14	$83,500	71%	$5,600
	Faculty Member	117	$69,000	46%	$4,000
	Academic Fieldwork Coordinator	25	$58,140	32%	$3,500
	Other	5	$74,000	100%	$14,000

(Continued)

Table 7.4. Annual Compensation, 9- or 10-Month Contract, Full-Time Employment: Academia Setting *(cont.)*

		Number of Responses	Median Compensation	Receiving Additional Cash Compensation	Median Additional Cash Compensation
Rank	Full Professor	30	$85,000	80%	$6,000
	Associate Professor	41	$76,000	63%	$4,500
	Assistant Professor	72	$64,500	40%	$4,000
	Instructor	26	$60,500	31%	$6,000
	Other	15	$60,000	40%	$7,750
Academic Responsibilities	For OT Program	134	$70,000	54%	$5,000
	For OTA Program	49	$61,000	41%	$6,000
	Other	1	—	—	—
Institution Type	Public	111	$69,000	52%	$5,000
	Private	73	$69,000	48%	$5,000

Note: — = insufficient data for analysis.

Table 7.5. Benefits Received: Academia Setting

	OT Full-Time	OT Part-Time	OTA Full-Time	OTA Part-Time
Sample Size	**565**	**27**	**26**	**5**
Health Insurance	86.4%	44.4%	84.6%	40%
Dental Insurance	79.1%	40.7%	88.5%	40%
Life Insurance	77.7%	33.3%	88.5%	40%
Professional Liability Insurance	34.2%	11.1%	19.2%	40%
Disability Insurance (Short- or Long-Term)	66.5%	33.3%	53.8%	0%
State Licensure	17.0%	3.7%	23.1%	0%
AOTA Member Dues	27.4%	11.1%	30.8%	20%
Continuing Education	81.9%	55.6%	80.8%	60%
College Tuition or Advanced Practice Certification	30.6%	3.7%	34.6%	0%
Paid Time Off (Vacation or Sick Leave)	82.8%	55.6%	80.8%	40%
Company-Paid Traditional Pension Plan	43.0%	37.0%	30.8%	20%
Employee-Funded Retirement Plan (e.g., 401K)	76.6%	44.4%	73.1%	40%

Module 8.
Setting Focus: Community

Table 8.1. Demographic Snapshot: Community Setting

		Community Setting	Full Sample
	Total Sample Size	**226**	**11,779**
	Median Age	**45**	**39**
Gender	Female	90.3%	90.9%
	Male	9.3%	8.8%
OT/OTA Status	OT	84.5%	82%
	OTA	15.5%	18%
Highest Degree Held in the Occupational Therapy Field	Certificate	0.4%	1.0%
	Associate's Degree	15.5%	16.8%
	Baccalaureate Degree	32.3%	26.6%
	Master's Degree	46.5%	49.4%
	Professional Doctorate Degree	4.0%	3.9%
	PhD	0.0%	0.9%
	ScD	0.0%	0.1%
	Other	1.3%	1.4%
Hold Advanced Certification/ Recognition	Currently Hold	21.7%	18.6%
	Pursuing	6.6%	5.2%
	Plan to Start	15.9%	18.2%
	No Plans to Start	55.8%	58.0%
Ethnic Background	African-American/Black	3.1%	3.1%
	American Indian/Alaskan Native	0.4%	0.3%
	Asian/Pacific Islander	7.1%	4.4%
	Caucasian/White	81.0%	85.3%
	Hispanic/Latino	1.8%	3.2%
	Multiethnic	1.3%	1.4%
	Prefer Not to Respond	5.3%	2.2%

(Continued)

Table 8.1. Demographic Snapshot: Community Setting *(cont.)*

		Community Setting	Full Sample
Total Years of Experience (Median)	Professional	12	9
	In Current Position at Current Setting	4	4
Region	Northeast	29.7%	22.1%
	South Atlantic	17.7%	17.7%
	South Central	13.3%	12.9%
	Noth Central	22.2%	29.0%
	Mountain	5.8%	7.3%
	Pacific	11.5%	11.9%
AOTA Member Status	Member	72.1%	58.6%
	Former Member	25.2%	37.2%
	Nonmember	2.7%	4.2%

Note: Percentages do not add to 100 due to rounding as well as "Other" and "Prefer not to answer" responses.

Table 8.2. Annual Compensation, Full-Time OTs: Community Setting

		Number of Responses	Median Compensation	Receiving Additional Cash Compensation	Median Additional Cash Received
	Overall	**149**	**$70,000**	**28%**	**$2,000**
Years of Professional Experience	0–5	34	$63,500	29%	$1,950
	5.1–10	34	$70,500	31%	$6,750
	10.1–15	14	$82,000	46%	$300
	15.1–25	34	$71,816	24%	$1,050
	25+	33	$68,000	17%	$2,750
Years in Current Position at Present Setting	0–2	33	$70,000	20%	$1,900
	2.1–5	54	$67,250	18%	$2,000
	5.1–10	24	$72,500	58%	$2,500
	10+	38	$70,000	26%	$1,300
Highest Degree Held in Occupational Therapy	Associate's Degree	1	—	0%	—
	Baccalaureate Degree	55	$71,000	28%	$2,750
	Master's Degree	85	$68,500	26%	$1,900
	Professional Doctorate Degree	7	$71,000	57%	$3,500
	Other	1	—	0%	—
Advanced Practice Certification/Recognition	Hold	33	$71,000	18%	$1,900
	Do Not Presently Hold	116	$69,000	27%	$2,000

(Continued)

Table 8.2. Annual Compensation, Full-Time OTs: Community Setting *(cont.)*

		Number of Responses	Median Compensation	Receiving Additional Cash Compensation	Median Additional Cash Received
Region	Northeast	52	$68,625	27%	$2,500
	South Atlantic	28	$70,500	32%	$1,200
	South Central	18	$68,500	31%	$4,000
	North Central	29	$62,000	14%	$3,750
	Mountain	9	$62,500	11%	—
	Pacific	13	$71,000	23%	$750
Setting Location	Urban	65	$70,000	19%	$2,000
	Suburban	69	$70,000	29%	$2,000
	Rural	15	$60,000	25%	$550
Control/Ownership	Government	24	$71,500	8%	—
	Private For Profit	67	$70,000	27%	$2,000
	Private Nonprofit	51	$68,125	27%	$1,500
	Unsure	7	$75,750	50%	$4,000
Employment Status	Employee	129	$68,125	29%	$2,000
	Contractor/Per Diem	11	$80,000	42%	$800
	Self-Employed	9	$92,500	0%	—

Note: Data are for respondents working 30 or more hours per week. — = insufficient data for tabulation.

Table 8.3. Annual Compensation, Full-Time OTAs: Community Setting

		Number of Responses	Median Compensation	Receiving Additional Cash Compensation	Median Additional Cash Received
	Overall	**28**	**$50,000**	**18%**	**$1,600**
Years of Professional Experience	0–5	16	$44,000	6%	—
	5.1–10	4	$51,900	25%	—
	10.1–15	2	—	50%	—
	15.1–25	4	$65,000	25%	—
	25+	2	—	50%	—
Years in Current Position at Present Setting	0–2	7	$41,500	14%	—
	2.1–5	16	$50,000	19%	$1,000
	5.1–10	0	—	0%	—
	10+	5	$65,000	20%	—
Highest Degree Held in Occupational Therapy	Associate's Degree	27	$49,000	19%	$1,600
	Other	1	—	—	—

(Continued)

Table 8.3. Annual Compensation, Full-Time OTAs: Community Setting *(cont.)*

		Number of Responses	Median Compensation	Receiving Additional Cash Compensation	Median Additional Cash Received
Advanced Practice Certification/Recognition	Hold	6	$54,000	17%	—
	Do Not Presently Hold	22	$48,000	14%	—
Region	Northeast	3	$52,000	0%	—
	South Atlantic	8	$55,000	13%	—
	South Central	6	$50,000	33%	—
	North Central	9	$45,000	11%	—
	Mountain	2	—	50%	—
	Pacific	0	—	0%	—
Setting Location	Urban	13	$53,800	23%	$1,600
	Suburban	9	$46,500	11%	—
	Rural	6	$41,000	16%	—
Control/Ownership	Government	4	$58,000	25%	—
	Private for Profit	16	$50,000	13%	—
	Private for Nonprofit	6	$47,500	33%	—
	Unsure	2	—	0%	—
Employment Status	Employee	25	$50,000	19%	$1,600
	Contractor/Per Diem	3	—	0%	—
	Self-Employed	0	—	0%	—

Note: Data are for respondents working 30 or more hours per week. — = insufficient data for tabulation.

Table 8.4. Part-Time Hourly Compensation, OTs: Community Setting

	Median Hours Worked	Median Hourly Rate	Number of Respondents	Receiving Additional Cash Compensation	Median Additional Cash Compensation
Total	**20.0**	**$50.00**	**12**	**0%**	**—**
Hourly Part-Time	20.0	$37.50	19	0%	—
Contractor/Per Diem	18.5	$50.00	18	0%	—
Self-Employed	20.0	$50.00	5	0%	—

Note: — = not applicable.

Table 8.5. Part-Time Hourly Compensation, OTAs: Community Setting

	Median Hours Worked	Median Hourly Rate	Number of Respondents	Receiving Additional Cash Compensation	Median Additional Cash Compensation
Total	**16**	**$26.00**	**7**	**0%**	**—**
Hourly Part-Time	22	$28.00	3	0%	—
Contractor/Per Diem	10	$25.50	4	0%	—

Note: — = not applicable.

Table 8.6. Benefits Received: Community Setting

	OT Full-Time	OT Part-Time	OTA Full-Time	OTA Part-Time
Sample Size	**149**	**42**	**28**	**7**
Health Insurance	67.8%	16.7%	75.0%	14.3%
Dental Insurance	67.8%	16.7%	75.0%	14.3%
Life Insurance	63.8%	14.3%	50.0%	0.0%
Professional Liability Insurance	51.0%	23.8%	25.0%	14.3%
Disability Insurance (Short- or Long-Term)	53.0%	11.9%	46.4%	0.0%
State Licensure	24.2%	4.8%	3.6%	14.3%
AOTA Member Dues	26.2%	9.5%	32.1%	0.0%
Continuing Education	61.1%	21.4%	60.7%	14.3%
College Tuition or Advanced Practice Certification	12.8%	4.8%	7.1%	0.0%
Paid Time Off (Vacation or Sick Leave)	81.9%	31.0%	85.7%	28.6%
Company-Paid Traditional Pension Plan	22.1%	2.4%	14.3%	0.0%
Employee-Funded Retirement Plan (e.g., 401K)	63.8%	23.8%	71.4%	14.3%

Module 9.
Setting Focus: Early Intervention

Table 9.1. Demographic Snapshot: Early Intervention Setting

	Early Intervention Setting	Full Sample
Total Sample Size	**501**	**11,779**
Median Age, Years	**38**	**39**
Gender		
Female	96.8%	90.9%
Male	3.2%	8.8%
OT/OTA Status		
OT	88.2%	82.0%
OTA	11.8%	18.0%
Highest Degree Held in Occupational Therapy		
Certificate	0.8%	1.0%
Associate's Degree	11.0%	16.8%
Baccalaureate Degree	27.9%	26.6%
Master's Degree	55.9%	49.4%
Professional Doctorate Degree	3.0%	3.9%
PhD	0.4%	0.9%
ScD	0.0%	0.1%
Other	1.0%	1.4%
Hold Advanced Certification/ Recognition		
Currently Hold	20.4%	18.6%
Pursuing	5.4%	5.2%
Plan to Start	20.6%	18.2%
No Plans to Start	53.7%	58.0%
Ethnic Background		
African-American/Black	2.2%	3.1%
American Indian/Alaskan Native	0.8%	0.3%
Asian/Pacific Islander	2.2%	4.4%
Caucasian/White	85.8%	85.3%
Hispanic/Latino	5.4%	3.2%
Multiethnic	1.0%	1.4%
Prefer Not to Respond	2.6%	2.2%

(Continued)

Table 9.1. Demographic Snapshot: Early Intervention Setting (cont.)

		Early Intervention Setting	Full Sample
Total Years of Experience (Median)	Professional	9	9
	In Current Position at Current Setting	4	4
Region	Northeast	27.4%	22.0%
	South Atlantic	14.8%	17.0%
	South Central	15.6%	12.9%
	North Central	18.4%	29.0%
	Mountain	9.2%	7.3%
	Pacific	14.8%	11.9%
AOTA Membership Status	Member	56.9%	58.6%
	Former Member	39.5%	37.2%
	Nonmember	3.6%	4.2%

Note: Percentages do not add to 100 due to rounding as well as "Other" and "Prefer not to answer" responses.

Table 9.2. Annual Compensation, Full-Time OTs: Early Intervention Setting

		Number of Responses	Median Compensation	Receiving Additional Cash Compensation	Median Additional Cash Received
	Overall	**291**	**$60,000**	**40.5%**	**$1,000**
Years of Professional Experience	0–5	115	$54,000	39.1%	$1,000
	5.1–10	46	$62,500	41.3%	$1,000
	10.1–15	39	$67,000	51.3%	$1,000
	15.1–25	46	$68,000	32.6%	$3,000
	25+	45	$70,000	42.2%	$950
Years in Current Position at Present Setting	0–2	83	$55,000	38.6%	$1,000
	2.1–5	101	$60,000	41.6%	$12,500
	5.1–10	25	$68,000	48.0%	$1,750
	10+	82	$70,000	39.0%	$1,000
Highest Degree Held in Occupational Therapy	Associate's Degree	1	—	100.0%	—
	Baccalaureate Degree	89	$68,000	37.1%	$1,050
	Master's Degree	188	$56,500	40.4%	$1,000
	Professional Doctorate Degree	11	$60,000	54.5%	$3,750
	Other	2	—	100.0%	—
Advanced Practice Certification/Recognition	Hold	59	$70,000	44.1%	$1,500
	Do Not Presently Hold	232	$58,500	39.7%	$1,000

(Continued)

Table 9.2. Annual Compensation, Full-Time OTs: Early Intervention Setting *(cont.)*

		Number of Responses	Median Compensation	Receiving Additional Cash Compensation	Median Additional Cash Received
Region	Northeast	79	$55,000	50.6%	$1,000
	South Atlantic	41	$63,000	39.0%	$1,100
	South Central	46	$62,000	41.3%	$1,000
	North Central	55	$58,000	29.1%	$1,500
	Mountain	27	$65,000	40.7%	$2,400
	Pacific	43	$65,000	37.2%	$1,000
Setting Location	Urban	127	$60,000	34.6%	$1,000
	Suburban	118	$60,000	45.8%	$1,200
	Rural	46	$60,000	43.5%	$900
Control/Ownership	Government	73	$58,000	31.5%	$1,000
	Private For Profit	101	$63,000	43.6%	$1,000
	Private Nonprofit	96	$59,000	42.7%	$960
	Other	8	$60,700	50.0%	$2,000
	Unsure	13	$55,000	46.2%	$1,650
Employment Status	Employee	251	$60,000	39.4%	$1,050
	Contractor	18	$67,500	94.4%	$500
	Self-Employed	22	$72,000	9.1%	—

Note: Data are for respondents working 30 or more hours per week. — = insufficient data for tabulation.

Table 9.3. Annual Compensation, Full-Time OTAs: Early Intervention Setting

		Number of Responses	Median Compensation	Receiving Additional Cash Compensation	Median Additional Cash Received
	Overall	**38**	**$40,000**	**26.3%**	**$375**
Years of Professional Experience	0–5	24	$39,500	20.8%	$150
	5.1–10	2	$48,442	50.0%	—
	10.1–15	6	$38,000	0.0%	—
	15.1–25	4	$35,690	75.0%	$1,000
	25+	2	$48,000	50.0%	—
Years in Current Position at Present Setting	0–2	15	$40,000	0.0%	—
	2.1–5	16	$37,000	50.0%	$625
	5.1–10	2	$44,000	0.0%	—
	10+	5	$42,000	40.0%	—

(Continued)

Table 9.3. Annual Compensation, Full-Time OTAs: Early Intervention Setting *(cont.)*

		Number of Responses	Median Compensation	Receiving Additional Cash Compensation	Median Additional Cash Received
Region	Northeast	5	$34,000	40.0%	—
	South Atlantic	3	$40,332	0.0%	—
	South Central	9	$50,000	33.3%	$150
	North Central	9	$33,000	33.3%	$150
	Mountain	8	$40,000	25.0%	—
	Pacific	4	$43,500	0.0%	—
Setting Location	Urban	17	$40,000	23.5%	$125
	Suburban	12	$35,500	16.7%	—
	Rural	9	$42,000	44.4%	$625
Control/Ownership	Government	9	$34,000	22.2%	—
	Private For Profit	16	$40,000	12.5%	—
	Private Nonprofit	7	$37,000	57.1%	$850
	Other	1	$35,500	100.0%	—
	Unsure	5	$54,500	20.0%	—
Employment Status	Employee	36	$40,000	27.8%	$375
	Contractor/Per Diem	2	—	0.0%	—
	Self-Employed	0	—	0.0%	—

Note: Data are for respondents working 30 or more hours per week. — = insufficient data for tabulation.

Table 9.4. Part-Time Hourly Compensation, OTs: Early Intervention Setting

	Median Hours Worked	Median Hourly Rate	Number of Respondents	Receiving Additional Cash Compensation	Median Additional Cash Compensation
Total	**18.0**	**$51.50**	**136**	**18%**	**$400**
Hourly Part-Time	21.0	$41.00	50	24%	$550
Contractor/Per Diem	15.0	$59.50	68	18%	$388
Self-Employed	20.0	$85.50	16	6%	$1,000
Other	9.5	—	2	0%	—

Note: — = insufficient data for tabulation.

Table 9.5. Part-Time Hourly Compensation, OTAs: Early Intervention Setting

	Median Hours Worked	Median Hourly Rate	Number of Respondents	Receiving Additional Cash Compensation	Median Additional Cash Compensation
Total	**20.0**	**$30.00**	**20**	**10%**	**$300**
Hourly Part-Time	16.0	$20.50	10	20%	$300
Contractor/Per Diem	20.0	$30.00	7	0%	—
Self-Employed	14.0	—	1	0%	—
Other	21.5	$54.00	2	0%	—

Note: — = insufficient data for tabulation.

Table 9.6. Benefits Received: Early Intervention Setting

	OT Full-Time	OT Part-Time	OTA Full-Time	OTA Part-Time
Sample Size	**291**	**136**	**38**	**20**
Health Insurance	63.9%	11.3%	60.5%	4.8%
Dental Insurance	57.4%	9.9%	52.6%	9.5%
Life Insurance	44.7%	9.3%	39.5%	9.5%
Professional Liability Insurance	47.4%	17.9%	36.8%	14.3%
Disability Insurance (Short- or Long-Term)	37.1%	10.6%	47.4%	4.8%
State Licensure	17.5%	7.3%	31.6%	4.8%
AOTA Member Dues	11.0%	7.3%	13.2%	0.0%
Continuing Education	62.5%	29.8%	65.8%	23.8%
College Tuition or Advanced Practice Certification	7.2%	1.3%	13.2%	0.0%
Paid Time Off (Vacation or Sick Leave)	77.3%	22.5%	78.9%	14.3%
Company-Paid Traditional Pension Plan	15.8%	4.6%	13.2%	0.0%
Employee-Funded Retirement Plan (e.g., 401K)	48.5%	19.9%	50.0%	19.0%

Module 10.
Setting Focus: Freestanding Outpatient

Table 10.1. Demographic Snapshot: Freestanding Outpatient Setting

		Freestanding Outpatient Setting	Full Sample
	Total Sample Size	**1,152**	**11,779**
	Median Age, Years	**36**	**39**
Gender	Female	91.0%	90.9%
	Male	8.9%	8.8%
OT/OTA Status	OT	90.3%	82.0%
	OTA	9.7%	18.0%
Highest Degree Held in Occupational Therapy	Certificate	1.1%	1.0%
	Associate's Degree	8.3%	16.8%
	Baccalaureate Degree	26.8%	26.6%
	Master's Degree	58.1%	49.4%
	Professional Doctorate Degree	3.9%	3.9%
	PhD	0.4%	0.9%
	ScD	0.0%	0.1%
	Other	1.4%	1.4%
Hold Advanced Certification/ Recognition	Currently Hold	33.8%	18.6%
	Pursuing	10.2%	5.2%
	Plan to Start	17.6%	18.2%
	No Plans to Start	38.5%	58.0%
Ethnic Background	African-American/Black	1.5%	3.1%
	American Indian/Alaskan Native	0.2%	0.3%
	Asian/Pacific Islander	3.7%	4.4%
	Caucasian/White	86.4%	85.3%
	Hispanic/Latino	4.6%	3.2%
	Multiethnic	1.7%	1.4%
	Prefer Not to Respond	2.1%	2.2%

(Continued)

Table 10.1. Demographic Snapshot: Freestanding Outpatient Setting *(cont.)*

		Freestanding Outpatient Setting	Full Sample
Total Years of Experience (Median)	Professional	7	9
	In Current Position at Current Setting	3	4
Region	Northeast	13.6%	22.1%
	South Atlantic	19.2%	17.0%
	South Central	17.4%	12.9%
	North Central	26.5%	29.0%
	Mountain	9.2%	7.3%
	Pacific	14.0%	11.9%
AOTA Membership Status	Member	60.2%	58.6%
	Former Member	36.4%	37.2%
	Nonmember	3.4%	4.2%

Note: Percentages do not add to 100 due to rounding as well as "Other" and "Prefer not to answer" responses.

Table 10.2. Annual Compensation, Full-Time OTs: Freestanding Outpatient Setting

		Number of Responses	Median Compensation	Receiving Additional Cash Compensation	Median Additional Cash Received
	Overall	**810**	**$65,000**	**36%**	**$1,000**
Years of Professional Experience	0–5	362	$60,000	42%	$1,000
	5.1–10	121	$68,000	37%	$1,000
	10.1–15	77	$71,000	30%	$1,000
	15.1–25	111	$75,000	31%	$2,500
	25+	139	$80,000	30%	$2,000
Years in Current Position at Present Setting	0–2	251	$60,000	38%	$1,000
	2.1–5	283	$64,000	40%	$1,000
	5.1–10	108	$72,000	35%	$1,000
	10+	168	$77,500	28%	$3,000
Highest Degree Held in Occupational Therapy	Associate's Degree	0	—	0%	—
	Baccalaureate Degree	228	$75,000	31%	$2,000
	Master's Degree	528	$62,000	38%	$1,000
	Professional Doctorate Degree	44	$71,000	34%	$1,000
	Other	10	$67,500	80%	$1,200
Advanced Practice Certification/Recognition	Hold	285	$75,00	33%	$2,000
	Do Not Presently Hold	525	$61,250	38%	$1,000

(Continued)

Table 10.2. Annual Compensation, Full-Time OTs: Freestanding Outpatient Setting *(cont.)*

		Number of Responses	Median Compensation	Receiving Additional Cash Compensation	Median Additional Cash Received
Region	Northeast	116	$67,000	30%	$1,000
	South Atlantic	132	$68,000	39%	$1,000
	South Central	144	$65,520	45%	$1,000
	North Central	236	$61,000	36%	$1,000
	Mountain	72	$64,000	35%	$1,100
	Pacific	110	$71,500	30%	$2,300
Setting Location	Urban	348	$66,000	38%	$1,000
	Suburban	363	$64,000	36%	$1,000
	Rural	99	$65,000	30%	$1,000
Control/Ownership	Government	39	$76,000	33%	$1,000
	Private For Profit	550	$65,434	39%	$1,000
	Private Nonprofit	189	$62,800	28%	$1,350
	Other	11	$75,000	45%	$1,000
	Unsure	21	$58,500	48%	$450
Employment Status	Employee	717	$65,000	3%	$500
	Contractor/Per Diem	29	$55,000	17%	$1,000
	Self-Employed	64	$80,000	18%	$2,000

Note: Data are for respondents working 30 or more hours per week. — = insufficient data for tabulation.

Table 10.3. Annual Compensation, Full-Time OTAs: Freestanding Outpatient Setting

		Number of Responses	Median Compensation	Receiving Additional Cash Compensation	Median Additional Cash Received
	Overall	**76**	**$43,100**	**28%**	**$500**
Years of Professional Experience	0–5	44	$42,219	34%	$500
	5.1–10	10	$50,500	50%	$300
	10.1–15	9	$45,000	0%	—
	15.1–25	9	$50,000	0%	—
	25+	4	$49,000	0%	—
Years in Current Position at Present Setting	0–2	22	$40,000	27%	$400
	2.1–5	33	$43,000	39%	$500
	5.1–10	8	$50,500	0%	—
	10+	13	$49,000	0%	—

(Continued)

Table 10.3. Annual Compensation, Full-Time OTAs: Freestanding Outpatient Setting *(cont.)*

		Number of Responses	Median Compensation	Receiving Additional Cash Compensation	Median Additional Cash Received
Highest Degree Held in Occupational Therapy	Associate's Degree	65	$43,000	22%	$300
	Baccalaureate Degree	2	$59,500	0%	—
	Master's Degree	3	$51,000	0%	—
	Professional Doctorate Degree	0	—	0%	—
	Other	6	$41,500	83%	$500
Advanced Practice Certification/Recognition	Hold	11	$48,000	36%	$1,000
	Do Not Presently Hold	65	$42,219	26%	$300
Region	Northeast	9	$45,000	0%	—
	South Atlantic	12	$43,500	50%	$225
	South Central	16	$52,000	31%	$500
	North Central	20	$40,000	0%	—
	Mountain	12	$45,500	50%	$1,100
	Pacific	7	$38,200	43%	$500
Setting Location	Urban	31	$45,000	23%	$500
	Suburban	33	$44,100	30%	$300
	Rural	12	$40,500	33%	$850
Control/Ownership	Government	2	$56,000	0%	—
	Private For Profit	47	$41,500	0%	—
	Private Nonprofit	19	$42,219	79%	$300
	Other	1	$52,000	0%	—
	Unsure	7	$47,500	0%	—
Employment Status	Employee	70	$44,100	0%	—
	Contractor/Per Diem	6	$48,500	33%	$300
	Self-Employed	0	—	0%	—

Note: Data are for respondents working 30 or more hours per week. — = insufficient data for tabulation.

Table 10.4. Part-Time Hourly Compensation, OTs: Freestanding Outpatient Setting

	Median Hours Worked	Median Hourly Rate	Number of Respondents	Receiving Additional Cash Compensation	Median Additional Cash Compensation
Total	**20**	**$42.00**	**206**	**22%**	**$500**
Hourly Part-Time	20	$39.00	111	26%	$500
Contractor/Per Diem	16	$48.00	71	20%	$400
Self-Employed	20	$80.00	21	5%	$100
Other	20	$25.00	3	33%	$100

Note: — = insufficient data for tabulation.

Table 10.5. Part-Time Hourly Compensation, OTAs: Freestanding Outpatient Setting

	Median Hours Worked	Median Hourly Rate	Number of Respondents	Receiving Additional Cash Compensation	Median Additional Cash Compensation
Total	**20.0**	**$26.50**	**35**	**9%**	**$150**
Hourly Part-Time	22.5	$24.50	14	14%	$125
Contractor/Per Diem	20.0	$31.00	19	5%	$2,208
Self-Employed	14.0	—	2	0%	$150

Note: — = insufficient data for tabulation.

Table 10.6. Benefits Received: Freestanding Outpatient Setting

	OT Full-Time	OT Part-Time	OTA Full-Time	OTA Part-Time
Sample Size	**810**	**206**	**76**	**35**
Health Insurance	71.2%	16.5%	65.8%	0.0%
Dental Insurance	58.0%	13.5%	47.4%	0.0%
Life Insurance	48.3%	11.7%	46.1%	0.0%
Professional Liability Insurance	64.0%	30.0%	44.7%	19.4%
Disability Insurance (Short- or Long-Term)	50.6%	11.7%	42.1%	5.6%
State Licensure	32.5%	13.9%	25.0%	0.0%
AOTA Member Dues	22.6%	13.9%	11.8%	0.0%
Continuing Education	78.1%	42.2%	65.8%	19.4%
College Tuition or Advanced Practice Certification	9.5%	3.0%	5.3%	0.0%
Paid Time Off (Vacation or Sick Leave)	84.2%	34.8%	80.3%	11.1%
Company-Paid Traditional Pension Plan	11.5%	4.8%	9.2%	2.8%
Employee-Funded Retirement Plan (e.g., 401K)	61.1%	28.3%	61.8%	8.3%

Module 11.
Setting Focus: Home Health

Table 11.1. Demographic Snapshot: Home Health Setting

		Home Health Setting	Full Sample
	Total Sample Size	**744**	**11,779**
	Median Age, Years	**43**	**39**
Gender	Female	87.8%	90.9%
	Male	11.7%	8.8%
OT/OTA Status	OT	87.9%	82.0%
	OTA	12.1%	18.0%
Highest Degree Held in Occupational Therapy	Certificate	1.3%	1.0%
	Associate's Degree	11.3%	16.8%
	Baccalaureate Degree	39.0%	26.6%
	Master's Degree	43.8%	49.4%
	Professional Doctorate Degree	2.7%	3.9%
	PhD	0.8%	0.9%
	ScD	0.0%	0.1%
	Other	1.1%	1.4%
Hold Advanced Certification/ Recognition	Currently Hold	18.2%	18.6%
	Pursuing	5.7%	5.2%
	Plan to Start	13.8%	18.2%
	No Plans to Start	62.4%	58.0%
Ethnic Background	African-American/Black	3.1%	3.1%
	American Indian/Alaskan Native	0.8%	0.3%
	Asian/Pacific Islander	3.2%	4.4%
	Caucasian/White	83.5%	85.3%
	Hispanic/Latino	4.7%	3.2%
	Multiethnic	1.9%	1.4%
	Prefer Not to Respond	2.8%	2.2%

(Continued)

Table 11.1. Demographic Snapshot: Home Health Setting *(cont.)*

		Home Health Setting	Full Sample
Total Years of Experience (Median)	Professional	12	9
	In Current Position at Current Setting	4	4
Region	Northeast	20.7%	22.0%
	South Atlantic	13.5%	17.0%
	South Central	20.4%	12.9%
	North Central	25.3%	29.4%
	Mountain	7.6%	7.3%
	Pacific	12.5%	11.9%
AOTA Membership Status	Member	54.7%	58.6%
	Former Member	41.7%	37.2%
	Nonmember	3.6%	4.2%

Note: Percentages do not add to 100 due to rounding as well as "Other" and "Prefer not to answer" responses.

Table 11.2. Annual Compensation, Full-Time OTs: Home Health Setting

		Number of Responses	Median Compensation	Receiving Additional Cash Compensation	Median Additional Cash Received
	Overall	**478**	**$76,000**	**35%**	**$1,500**
Years of Professional Experience	0–5	120	$70,000	36%	$1,200
	5.1–10	86	$75,000	34%	$1,500
	10.1–15	76	$80,000	37%	$1,100
	15.1–25	118	$79,000	30%	$1,000
	25+	78	$80,000	44%	$2,000
Years in Current Position at Present Setting	0–2	103	$75,000	27%	$1,200
	2.1–5	183	$75,173	42%	$3,000
	5.1–10	76	$80,000	36%	$1,500
	10+	116	$80,000	33%	$1,000
Highest Degree Held in Occupational Therapy	Associate's Degree	0	—	0%	—
	Baccalaureate Degree	201	$80,000	33%	$2,000
	Master's Degree	245	$75,000	36%	$2,500
	Professional Doctorate Degree	20	$75,000	45%	$3,100
	Other	12	$50,000	42%	$1,500
Advanced Practice Certification/Recognition	Hold	92	$80,000	30%	$1,500
	Do Not Presently Hold	386	$76,000	37%	$2,000

(Continued)

Table 11.2. Annual Compensation, Full-Time OTs: Home Health Setting *(cont.)*

		Number of Responses	Median Compensation	Receiving Additional Cash Compensation	Median Additional Cash Received
Region	Northeast	106	$75,000	34%	$2,000
	South Atlantic	64	$83,000	41%	$2,250
	South Central	86	$87,000	36%	$1,100
	North Central	117	$68,000	43%	$1,200
	Mountain	38	$63,000	34%	$1,500
	Pacific	67	$75,850	19%	$2,000
Setting Location	Urban	174	$80,000	33%	$1,375
	Suburban	193	$75,000	38%	$1,000
	Rural	111	$75,000	33%	$3,750
Control/Ownership	Government	26	$72,000	15%	$2,000
	Private For Profit	248	$80,000	35%	$1,000
	Private Nonprofit	175	$73,000	38%	—
	Other	2	$105,000	50%	$2,000
	Unsure	27	$72,000	41%	$1,500
Employment Status	Employee	424	$76,000	36%	$1,000
	Contractor/Per Diem	35	$66,500	37%	$4,900
	Self-Employed	19	$81,000	16%	—

Note: Data are for respondents working 30 or more hours per week. — = insufficient data for tabulation.

Table 11.3. Annual Compensation, Full-Time OTAs: Home Health Setting

		Number of Responses	Median Compensation	Receiving Additional Cash Compensation	Median Additional Cash Received
	Overall	**60**	**$50,000**	**35%**	**$1,500**
Years of Professional Experience	0–5	17	$50,000	53%	$4,000
	5.1–10	19	$54,000	26%	$3,000
	10.1–15	5	$52,000	60%	$1,200
	15.1–25	15	$50,000	13%	$200
	25+	4	$38,000	50%	$2,750
Years in Current Position at Present Setting	0–2	12	$54,000	50%	$4,500
	2.1–5	27	$50,000	37%	$2,500
	5.1–10	14	$50,000	29%	$650
	10+	7	$50,000	14%	—

(Continued)

Table 11.3. Annual Compensation, Full-Time OTAs: Home Health Setting *(cont.)*

		Number of Responses	Median Compensation	Receiving Additional Cash Compensation	Median Additional Cash Received
Highest Degree Held in Occupational Therapy	Associate's Degree	57	$50,000	35%	$1,350
	Baccalaureate Degree	1	—	0%	—
	Master's Degree	—	—	0%	—
	Professional Doctorate Degree	—	—	0%	—
	Other	2	—	0%	—
Advanced Practice Certification/Recognition	Hold	8	$54,500	13%	—
	Do Not Presently Hold	52	$50,000	38%	$1,350
Region	Northeast	4	$44,000	25%	—
	South Atlantic	9	$54,000	22%	—
	South Central	24	$55,000	33%	$3,000
	North Central	18	$40,500	50%	$1,000
	Mountain	3	$37,500	33%	—
	Pacific	2	$43,500	50%	—
Setting Location	Urban	23	$54,500	35%	$1,375
	Suburban	18	$51,000	39%	$1,500
	Rural	19	$50,000	32%	$2,000
Control/Ownership	Government	5	$52,000	60%	$2,000
	Private For Profit	39	$54,000	39%	$1,500
	Private Nonprofit	11	$46,500	30%	$500
	Other	1	—	100%	—
	Unsure	4	$50,000	100%	—
Employment Status	Employee	47	$50,000	38%	$1,350
	Contractor/Per Diem	9	$65,000	22%	—
	Self-Employed	4	$70,000	25%	—

Note: Data are for respondents working 30 or more hours per week. — = insufficient data for tabulation.

Table 11.4. Part-TIme Hourly Compensation, OTs: Home Health Setting

	Median Hours Worked	Median Hourly Rate	Number of Respondents	Receiving Additional Cash Compensation	Median Additional Cash Compensation
Total	**20**	**$50.00**	**163**	**11%**	**$565**
Hourly Part-Time	20	$43.50	70	16%	$600
Contractor/Per Diem	20	$55.00	73	7%	$500
Self-Employed	11	$64.00	14	7%	$2,000
Other	12	$57.00	6	17%	$4,900

Note: — = insufficient data for tabulation.

Table 11.5. Part-Time Hourly Compensation, OTAs: Home Health Setting

	Median Hours Worked	Median Hourly Rate	Number of Respondents	Receiving Additional Cash Compensation	Median Additional Cash Compensation
Total	**21**	**$30.00**	**30**	**13%**	**$5,500**
Hourly Part-Time	20	$28.00	12	25%	$5,000
Contractor/Per Diem	24	$41.00	13	8%	$13,000
Self-Employed	24	—	1	0%	—
Other	20	$50.00	4	0%	—

Note: — = insufficient data for tabulation.

Table 11.6. Benefits Received: Home Health Setting

	OT Full-Time	OT Part-Time	OTA Full-Time	OTA Part-Time
Sample Size	**478**	**163**	**60**	**30**
Health Insurance	72.8%	22.3%	60.0%	16.7%
Dental Insurance	69.2%	22.9%	60.0%	20.0%
Life Insurance	65.9%	18.9%	53.3%	10.0%
Professional Liability Insurance	43.5%	16.0%	41.7%	10.0%
Disability Insurance (Short- or Long-Term)	61.3%	18.9%	36.7%	20.0%
State Licensure	13.0%	2.9%	16.7%	6.7%
AOTA Member Dues	6.7%	2.9%	8.3%	3.3%
Continuing Education	43.3%	20.0%	40.0%	13.3%
College Tuition or Advanced Practice Certification	10.3%	0.6%	6.7%	0.0%
Paid Time Off (Vacation or Sick Leave)	84.9%	33.7%	68.3%	26.7%
Company-Paid Traditional Pension Plan	18.0%	5.7%	8.3%	10.0%
Employee-Funded Retirement Plan (e.g., 401K)	68.6%	30.9%	40.0%	20.0%

Module 12.
Setting Focus: Hospital (Non–Mental Health)

Table 12.1. Demographic Snapshot: Hospital (Non–Mental Health) Setting

		Hospital (Non–Mental Health) Setting	Full Sample
	Total Sample Size	**2,812**	**11,779**
	Median Age, Years	**35**	**39**
Gender	Female	91.9%	90.9%
	Male	7.9%	8.8%
OT/OTA Status	OT	91.5%	82.0%
	OTA	8.5%	18.0%
Highest Degree Held in Occupational Therapy	Certificate	0.5%	1.0%
	Associate's Degree	7.9%	16.8%
	Baccalaureate Degree	28.3%	26.6%
	Master's Degree	57.7%	49.4%
	Professional Doctorate Degree	4.1%	3.9%
	PhD	0.2%	0.9%
	ScD	0.1%	0.1%
	Other	1.2%	1.4%
Hold Advanced Certification/ Recognition	Currently Hold	22.5%	18.6%
	Pursuing	6.6%	5.2%
	Plan to Start	19.7%	18.2%
	No Plans to Start	51.3%	58.0%
Ethnic Background	African-American/Black	2.6%	3.1%
	American Indian/Alaskan Native	0.1%	0.3%
	Asian/Pacific Islander	5.5%	4.4%
	Caucasian/White	86.2%	85.3%
	Hispanic/Latino	2.7%	3.2%
	Multiethnic	0.9%	1.4%
	Prefer Not to Respond	2.0%	2.2%

(Continued)

Table 12.1. Demographic Snapshot: Hospital (Non–Mental Health) Setting *(cont.)*

		Hospital (Non–Mental Health) Setting	Full Sample
Total Years of Experience (Median)	Professional	7	9
	In Current Position at Current Setting	4	4
Region	Northeast	16.3%	22.1%
	South Atlantic	17.7%	17.0%
	South Central	14.2%	12.9%
	North Central	32.5%	29.0%
	Mountain	7.6%	7.3%
	Pacific	11.7%	11.9%
AOTA Membership Status	Member	56.7%	58.6%
	Former Member	39.4%	37.2%
	Nonmember	3.9%	4.2%

Note: Percentages do not add to 100 due to rounding as well as "Other" and "Prefer not to answer" responses.

Table 12.2. Annual Compensation, Full-Time OTs: Hospital (Non–Mental Health) Setting

		Number of Responses	Median Compensation	Receiving Additional Cash Compensation	Median Additional Cash Received
	Overall	**2,225**	**$68,000**	**35%**	**$1,000**
Years of Professional Experience	0–5	944	$61,000	32%	$1,200
	5.1–10	388	$67,000	33%	$675
	10.1–15	254	$75,000	40%	$1,000
	15.1–25	346	$82,000	39%	$1,000
	25+	293	$84,000	42%	$1,200
Years in Current Position at Present Setting	0–2	506	$62,000	29%	$2,000
	2.1–5	916	$65,000	34%	$850
	5.1–10	286	$74,000	38%	$1,000
	10+	517	$80,000	42%	$1,000
Highest Degree Held in Occupational Therapy	Associate's Degree	1	—	100%	—
	Baccalaureate Degree	639	$80,000	40%	$1,000
	Master's Degree	1,446	$65,000	33%	$1,000
	Professional Doctorate Degree	110	$71,000	36%	$1,300
	Other	29	$81,000	52%	$800
Advanced Practice Certification/Recognition	Hold	529	$78,000	42%	$1,100
	Do Not Presently Hold	1,696	$65,000	33%	$1,000

(Continued)

Table 12.2. Annual Compensation, Full-Time OTs: Hospital (Non–Mental Health) Setting *(cont.)*

		Number of Responses	Median Compensation	Receiving Additional Cash Compensation	Median Additional Cash Received
Region	Northeast	380	$69,000	27%	$1,100
	South Atlantic	403	$68,889	39%	$1,000
	South Central	325	$68,000	34%	$1,000
	North Central	705	$65,000	37%	$1,000
	Mountain	162	$65,000	39%	$800
	Pacific	250	$79,000	38%	$1,000
Setting Location	Urban	1,286	$68,000	34%	$1,000
	Suburban	616	$67,000	37%	$1,000
	Rural	323	$69,000	40%	$1,000
Control/Ownership	Government	279	$73,000	36%	$1,250
	Private For Profit	406	$67,000	28%	$1,500
	Private Nonprofit	1,394	$67,200	38%	$1,000
	Other	37	$69,000	46%	$950
	Unsure	109	$63,500	26%	—
Employment Status	Employee	2,118	$68,000	36%	$1,000
	Contractor/Per Diem	94	$67,000	34%	$450
	Self-Employed	13	$65,000	23%	$2,100

Note: Data are for respondents working 30 or more hours per week. — = insufficient data for tabulation.

Table 12.3. Annual Compensation, Full-Time OTAs: Hospital (Non–Mental Health) Setting

		Number of Responses	Median Compensation	Receiving Additional Cash Compensation	Median Additional Cash Received
	Overall	**192**	**$43,000**	**26%**	**$500**
Years of Professional Experience	0–5	86	$40,000	28%	$500
	5.1–10	38	$43,000	34%	$300
	10.1–15	16	$50,000	25%	$800
	15.1–25	35	$49,000	17%	$775
	25+	17	$46,000	18%	$500
Years in Current Position at Present Setting	0–2	44	$40,000	16%	$500
	2.1–5	77	$43,000	34%	$500
	5.1–10	24	$45,000	33%	$300
	10+	47	$47,000	19%	$500

(Continued)

Table 12.3. Annual Compensation, Full-Time OTAs: Hospital (Non–Mental Health) Setting *(cont.)*

		Number of Responses	Median Compensation	Receiving Additional Cash Compensation	Median Additional Cash Received
Highest Degree Held in Occupational Therapy	Associate's Degree	173	$42,000	26%	$500
	Baccalaureate Degree	5	$49,000	20%	—
	Master's Degree	1	—	0%	—
	Professional Doctorate Degree	0	—	0%	—
	Other	13	$47,000	0%	—
Advanced Practice Certification/Recognition	Hold	17	$45,000	12%	$1,850
	Do Not Presently Hold	175	$43,000	27%	$500
Region	Northeast	17	$43,000	18%	$175
	South Atlantic	30	$40,000	23%	$350
	South Central	31	$46,734	26%	$1,000
	North Central	86	$43,000	24%	$500
	Mountain	15	$40,000	40%	$538
	Pacific	13	$50,000	38%	$875
Setting Location	Urban	104	$45,000	27%	$500
	Suburban	61	$42,000	18%	$350
	Rural	27	$42,000	41%	$500
Control/Ownership	Government	25	$47,000	28%	$300
	Private For Profit	56	$44,250	21%	$500
	Private Nonprofit	84	$42,000	30%	$500
	Other	3	$46,853	0%	—
	Unsure	24	$39,500	25%	$400
Employment Status	Employee	179	$43,250	26%	$500
	Contractor/Per Diem	11	$36,000	36%	$500
	Self-Employed	2	$26,500	0%	—

Note: Data are for respondents working 30 or more hours per week. — = insufficient data for tabulation.

Table 12.4. Part-Time Hourly Compensation, OTs: Hospital (Non–Mental Health) Setting

	Median Hours Worked	Median Hourly Rate	Number of Respondents	Receiving Additional Cash Compensation	Median Additional Cash Compensation
Total	**20**	**$40.00**	**300**	**19%**	**$500**
Hourly Part-Time	24	$37.00	147	28%	$600
Contractor/Per Diem	16	$44.00	147	11%	$250
Other	24	$40.50	6	0%	—

Note: — = insufficient data for tabulation.

Table 12.5. Part-Time Hourly Compensation, OTAs: Hospital (Non–Mental Health) Setting

	Median Hours Worked	Median Hourly Rate	Number of Respondents	Receiving Additional Cash Compensation	Median Additional Cash Compensation
Total	**20**	**$25.50**	**48**	**19%**	**$250**
Hourly Part-Time	24	$23.00	17	35%	$200
Contractor/Per Diem	20	$26.50	28	11%	$1,250
Other	24	$30.00	3	0%	—

Note: — = insufficient data for tabulation.

Table 12.6. Benefits Received: Hospital (Non–Mental Health) Setting

	OT Full-Time	OT Part-Time	OTA Full-Time	OTA Part-Time
Sample Size	**2,225**	**300**	**192**	**48**
Health Insurance	86.8%	36.0%	80.2%	16.7%
Dental Insurance	83.5%	35.2%	75.5%	16.7%
Life Insurance	76.9%	32.9%	64.1%	12.5%
Professional Liability Insurance	58.3%	28.8%	47.9%	16.7%
Disability Insurance (Short- or Long-Term)	74.6%	32.6%	65.6%	12.5%
State Licensure	10.1%	2.6%	14.1%	8.3%
AOTA Member Dues	12.9%	2.6%	10.9%	8.3%
Continuing Education	66.1%	39.8%	57.8%	16.7%
College Tuition or Advanced Practice Certification	21.5%	5.8%	19.3%	6.3%
Paid Time Off (Vacation or Sick Leave)	92.7%	51.3%	93.2%	29.2%
Company-Paid Traditional Pension Plan	29.7%	14.7%	29.2%	4.2%
Employee-Funded Retirement Plan (e.g., 401K)	83.7%	59.4%	78.6%	33.3%

Module 13.
Setting Focus: Long-Term Care/ Skilled-Nursing Facility

Table 13.1. Demographic Snapshot: LTC/SNF Setting

		LTC/SNF Setting	Full Sample
	Total Sample Size	**3,038**	**11,779**
	Median Age, Years	**37**	**39**
Gender	Female	88.1%	90.9%
	Male	11.7%	8.8%
OT/OTA Status	OT	61.1%	82.0%
	OTA	38.9%	18.0%
Highest Degree Held in Occupational Therapy	Certificate	1.4%	1.0%
	Associate's Degree	36.5%	16.8%
	Baccalaureate Degree	18.0%	26.6%
	Master's Degree	41.4%	49.4%
	Professional Doctorate Degree	1.7%	3.9%
	PhD	0.1%	0.9%
	ScD	0.0%	0.1%
	Other	0.8%	1.4%
Hold Advanced Certification/ Recognition	Currently Hold	8.0%	18.6%
	Pursuing	4.1%	5.2%
	Plan to Start	23.2%	18.2%
	No Plans to Start	64.7%	58.0%
Ethnic Background	African-American/Black	4.6%	3.1%
	American Indian/Alaskan Native	0.4%	0.3%
	Asian/Pacific Islander	5.7%	4.4%
	Caucasian/White	82.7%	85.3%
	Hispanic/Latino	2.7%	3.2%
	Multiethnic	1.7%	1.4%
	Prefer Not to Respond	2.2%	2.2%

(Continued)

Table 13.1. Demographic Snapshot: LTC/SNF Setting *(cont.)*

		LTC/SNF Setting	Full Sample
Total Years of Experience (Median)	Professional	6	9
	In Current Position at Current Setting	3	4
Region	Northeast	22.7%	22.0%
	South Atlantic	16.7%	17.0%
	South Central	11.6%	12.9%
	North Central	31.4%	29.0%
	Mountain	6.2%	7.3%
	Pacific	11.4%	11.9%
AOTA Membership Status	Member	50.8%	58.6%
	Former Member	43.0%	37.2%
	Nonmember	6.2%	4.2%

Note: Percentages do not add to 100 due to rounding as well as "Other" and "Prefer not to answer" responses.

Table 13.2. Annual Compensation, Full-Time OTs: LTC/SNF Setting

		Number of Responses	Median Compensation	Receiving Additional Cash Compensation	Median Additional Cash Received
	Overall	**1,624**	**$73,000**	**24%**	**$1,500**
Years of Professional Experience	0–5	758	$69,000	23%	$1,000
	5.1–10	291	$72,000	24%	$1,500
	10.1–15	197	$78,000	25%	$2,000
	15.1–25	243	$83,360	24%	$2,200
	25+	135	$84,000	24%	$1,477
Years in Current Position at Present Setting	0–2	499	$69,000	22%	$1,700
	2.1–5	632	$72,000	24%	$1,032
	5.1–10	212	$77,396	22%	$1,500
	10+	281	$83,000	25%	$1,500
Highest Degree Held in Occupational Therapy	Associate's Degree	1	—	100%	—
	Baccalaureate Degree	441	$80,000	24%	$1,500
	Master's Degree	1,112	$70,000	23%	$1,060
	Professional Doctorate Degree	51	$75,500	29%	$1,500
	Other	19	$75,000	21%	$1,500
Advanced Practice Certification/Recognition	Hold	164	$76,500	25%	$1,500
	Do Not Presently Hold	1,460	$72,000	23%	$1,500

(Continued)

Table 13.2. Annual Compensation, Full-Time OTs: LTC/SNF Setting *(cont.)*

		Number of Responses	Median Compensation	Receiving Additional Cash Compensation	Median Additional Cash Received
Region	Northeast	384	$70,000	18%	$1,500
	South Atlantic	280	$76,330	26%	$1,500
	South Central	193	$76,000	28%	$1,500
	North Central	451	$70,000	26%	$1,110
	Mountain	94	$75,000	24%	$2,000
	Pacific	222	$80,000	21%	$2,000
Setting Location	Urban	543	$74,000	21%	$1,500
	Suburban	744	$72,000	22%	$1,500
	Rural	337	$72,000	31%	$1,450
Control/Ownership	Government	89	$70,000	33%	$1,000
	Private For Profit	1,077	$75,000	22%	$1,800
	Private Nonprofit	285	$70,000	28%	$1,200
	Other	10	$76,500	30%	$300
	Unsure	163	$68,000	17%	$900
Employment Status	Employee	1,532	$73,000	23%	$1,500
	Contractor/Per Diem	85	$67,000	28%	$2,000
	Self-Employed	7	$82,000	43%	$10,000

Note: Data are for respondents working 30 or more hours per week. — = insufficient data for tabulation.

Table 13.3. Annual Compensation, Full-Time OTAs: LTC/SNF Setting

		Number of Responses	Median Compensation	Receiving Additional Cash Compensation	Median Additional Cash Received
	Overall	**1,008**	**$5,000**	**18%**	**$500**
Years of Professional Experience	0–5	538	$46,900	18%	$600
	5.1–10	191	$50,000	17%	$500
	10.1–15	102	$50,000	20%	$500
	15.1–25	142	$55,000	19%	$750
	25+	35	$53,500	17%	$65
Years in Current Position at Present Setting	0–2	263	$45,000	16%	$550
	2.1–5	438	$50,000	19%	$600
	5.1–10	158	$50,000	18%	$500
	10+	149	$50,500	19%	$500

(Continued)

Table 13.3. Annual Compensation, Full-Time OTAs: LTC/SNF Setting *(cont.)*

		Number of Responses	Median Compensation	Receiving Additional Cash Compensation	Median Additional Cash Received
Highest Degree Held in Occupational Therapy	Associate's Degree	944	$49,460	18%	$550
	Baccalaureate Degree	21	$50,000	24%	$1,000
	Master's Degree	5	$50,000	20%	—
	Professional Doctorate Degree	0	—	0%	—
	Other	38	$60,000	24%	$500
Advanced Practice Certification/Recognition	Hold	50	$47,000	24%	$400
	Do Not Presently Hold	958	$50,000	18%	$600
Region	Northeast	201	$47,000	14%	$1,000
	South Atlantic	163	$53,000	18%	$500
	South Central	124	$50,000	22%	$500
	North Central	380	$46,000	18%	$500
	Mountain	61	$50,000	23%	$1,150
	Pacific	79	$53,000	18%	$800
Setting Location	Urban	356	$50,000	14%	$500
	Suburban	410	$50,000	20%	$550
	Rural	242	$48,000	21%	$775
Control/Ownership	Government	67	$48,000	12%	$1,750
	Private For Profit	635	$50,000	18%	$500
	Private Nonprofit	153	$48,000	20%	$550
	Other	12	$40,000	17%	$175
	Unsure	141	$47,000	18%	$800
Employment Status	Employee	949	$50,000	18%	$500
	Contractor/Per Diem	52	$41,250	19%	$1,200
	Self-Employed	7	$46,000	57%	$13,500

Note: Data are for respondents working 30 or more hours per week. — = insufficient data for tabulation.

Table 13.4. Part-Time Hourly Compensation, OTs: LTC/SNF Setting

	Median Hours Worked	Median Hourly Rate	Number of Respondents	Receiving Additional Cash Compensation	Median Additional Cash Compensation
Total	**20**	**$45.00**	**226**	**9%**	**$250**
Hourly Part-Time	22	$39.00	79	14%	$225
Contractor/Per Diem	16	$50.00	137	7%	$275
Self-Employed	10	$75.00	1	0%	—
Other	15	$45.00	9	0%	—

Note: — = insufficient data for tabulation.

Table 13.5. Part-Time Hourly Compensation, OTAs: LTC/SNF Setting

	Median Hours Worked	Median Hourly Rate	Number of Respondents	Receiving Additional Cash Compensation	Median Additional Cash Compensation
Total	**20**	**$30.00**	**173**	**7%**	**$500**
Hourly Part-Time	24	$26.00	57	11%	$100
Contractor/Per Diem	16	$31.00	105	4%	$800
Self-Employed	15	—	1	0%	—
Other	15	$29.50	10	20%	$1,750

Note: — = insufficient data for tabulation.

Table 13.6. Benefits Received: LTC/SNF Setting

	OT Full-Time	OT Part-Time	OTA Full-Time	OTA Part-Time
Sample Size	**1,624**	**226**	**1,008**	**173**
Health Insurance	75.1%	11.2%	71.5%	8.0%
Dental Insurance	72.7%	12.5%	68.9%	7.5%
Life Insurance	63.6%	8.2%	65.2%	5.7%
Professional Liability Insurance	44.8%	18.1%	40.2%	10.3%
Disability Insurance (Short- or Long-Term)	56.9%	8.6%	58.8%	10.9%
State Licensure	29.9%	3.9%	33.0%	9.2%
AOTA Member Dues	21.7%	3.9%	20.7%	5.2%
Continuing Education	60.4%	19.4%	57.8%	21.3%
College Tuition or Advanced Practice Certification	6.3%	3.0%	8.0%	3.4%
Paid Time Off (Vacation or Sick Leave)	89.7%	30.2%	88.7%	27.0%
Company-Paid Traditional Pension Plan	6.5%	1.3%	8.8%	1.7%
Employee-Funded Retirement Plan (e.g., 401K)	63.4%	21.6%	57.2%	19.5%

Module 14.
Setting Focus: Mental Health

Table 14.1. Demographic Snapshot: Mental Health Setting

		Mental Health Setting	Full Sample
	Total Sample Size	**261**	**11,779**
	Median Age, Years	**41**	**39**
Gender	Female	90.0%	90.9%
	Male	10.0%	8.8%
OT/OTA Status	OT	88.5%	82.0%
	OTA	11.5%	18.0%
Highest Degree Held in Occupational Therapy	Certificate	0.0%	1.0%
	Associate's Degree	11.9%	16.8%
	Baccalaureate Degree	26.8%	26.6%
	Master's Degree	56.7%	49.4%
	Professional Doctorate Degree	2.3%	3.9%
	PhD	0.0%	0.9%
	ScD	0.4%	0.1%
	Other	1.9%	1.4%
Hold Advanced Certification/ Recognition	Currently Hold	5.4%	18.6%
	Pursuing	3.5%	5.2%
	Plan to Start	20.7%	18.2%
	No Plans to Start	70.5%	58.0%
Ethnic Background	African-American/Black	3.5%	3.1%
	American Indian/Alaskan Native	0.4%	0.3%
	Asian/Pacific Islander	2.7%	4.4%
	Caucasian/White	84.3%	85.3%
	Hispanic/Latino	4.2%	3.2%
	Multiethnic	1.5%	1.4%
	Prefer Not to Respond	3.5%	2.2%

(Continued)

Table 14.1. Demographic Snapshot: Mental Health Setting *(cont.)*

		Mental Health Setting	Full Sample
Total Years of Experience (Median)	Professional	10	9
	In Current Position at Current Setting	4	4
Region	Northeast	30.0%	22.0%
	South Atlantic	13.5%	17.0%
	South Central	7.7%	12.9%
	North Central	25.7%	29.0%
	Mountain	5.0%	7.3%
	Pacific	18.1%	11.9%
AOTA Membership Status	Member	70.9%	58.6%
	Former Member	26.4%	37.2%
	Nonmember	2.7%	4.2%

Note: Percentages do not add to 100 due to rounding as well as "Other" and "Prefer not to answer" responses.

Table 14.2. Annual Compensation, Full-Time OTs: Mental Health Setting

		Number of Responses	Median Compensation	Receiving Additional Cash Compensation	Median Additional Cash Received
	Overall	**206**	**$69,000**	**19%**	**$800**
Years of Professional Experience	0–5	70	$58,000	21%	$800
	5.1–10	31	$69,680	19%	$600
	10.1–15	31	$71,000	29%	$1,300
	15.1–25	35	$79,000	17%	$630
	25+	39	$80,000	10%	$225
Years in Current Position at Present Setting	0–2	49	$58,000	14%	$600
	2.1–5	69	$65,000	20%	$800
	5.1–10	32	$76,500	22%	$900
	10+	56	$77,110	21%	$630
Highest Degree Held in Occupational Therapy	Associate's Degree	1	—	0%	—
	Baccalaureate Degree	63	$76,900	22%	$650
	Master's Degree	132	$64,000	19%	$800
	Professional Doctorate Degree	6	$80,000	17%	—
	Other	4	$75,000	0%	—
Advanced Practice Certification/Recognition	Hold	11	$66,000	36%	$2,500
	Do Not Presently Hold	195	$69,340	18%	$675

(Continued)

Table 14.2. Annual Compensation, Full-Time OTs: Mental Health Setting *(cont.)*

		Number of Responses	Median Compensation	Receiving Additional Cash Compensation	Median Additional Cash Received
Region	Northeast	68	$69,000	16%	$2,000
	South Atlantic	27	$69,680	7%	—
	South Central	17	$82,000	35%	$550
	North Central	49	$61,000	22%	$600
	Mountain	9	$68,000	11%	—
	Pacific	36	$70,000	25%	$1,000
Setting Location	Urban	130	$69,000	22%	$775
	Suburban	57	$69,000	18%	$1,900
	Rural	19	$67,000	11%	—
Control/Ownership	Government	105	$71,000	12%	$1,200
	Private For Profit	19	$69,888	16%	$2,000
	Private Nonprofit	77	$65,000	27%	$600
	Other	1	—	100%	—
	Unsure	4	$65,000	50%	—
Employment Status	Employee	204	$69,000	19%	$800
	Contractor/Per Diem	1	—	0%	—
	Self-Employed	1	—	100%	—

Note: Data are for respondents working 30 or more hours per week. — = insufficient data for tabulation.

Table 14.3. Annual Compensation, Full-Time OTAs: Mental Health Setting

		Number of Responses	Median Compensation	Receiving Additional Cash Compensation	Median Additional Cash Received
	Overall	**23**	**$45,000**	**30%**	**$1,000**
Years of Professional Experience	0–5	12	$45,206	8%	—
	5.1–10	4	$40,511	50%	—
	10.1–15	1	$44,000	0%	—
	15.1–25	3	$52,000	67%	—
	25+	3	$37,000	67%	—
Years in Current Position at Present Setting	0–2	5	$45,411	0%	—
	2.1–5	8	$45,000	25%	—
	5.1–10	5	$40,000	60%	$1,000
	10+	5	$50,000	40%	—

(Continued)

Table 14.3. Annual Compensation, Full-Time OTAs: Mental Health Setting *(cont.)*

		Number of Responses	Median Compensation	Receiving Additional Cash Compensation	Median Additional Cash Received
Highest Degree Held in Occupational Therapy	Associate's Degree	23	$45,000	30%	$1,000
	Baccalaureate Degree	0	—	0%	—
	Master's Degree	0	—	0%	—
	Professional Doctorate Degree	0	—	0%	—
	Other	0	—	0%	
Advanced Practice Certification/Recognition	Hold	1	—	0%	—
	Do Not Presently Hold	22	$45,000	27%	$1,100
Region	Northeast	5	$52,000	40%	—
	South Atlantic	1	—	0%	—
	South Central	3	$50,000	0%	—
	North Central	10	$36,500	40%	$875
	Mountain	3	$48,000	0%	—
	Pacific	1	—	100%	—
Setting Location	Urban	16	$47,500	38%	$1,100
	Suburban	4	$45,206	0%	—
	Rural	3	$16,000	33%	—
Control/Ownership	Government	12	$45,206	33%	$875
	Private For Profit	7	$45,000	14%	—
	Private Nonprofit	4	$44,000	50%	—
	Other	0	—	0%	—
	Unsure	0	—	0%	—
Employment Status	Employee	23	$45,000	30%	$1,000
	Contractor/Per Diem	0	—	0%	—
	Self-Employed	0	—	0%	—

Note: Data are for respondents working 30 or more hours per week. — = insufficient data for tabulation.

Table 14.4. Part-Time Hourly Compensation, OTs: Mental Health Setting

	Median Hours Worked	Median Hourly Rate	Number of Respondents	Receiving Additional Cash Compensation	Median Additional Cash Compensation
Total	**20**	**$42.00**	**21**	**14%**	**$250**
Hourly Part-Time	20	$36.00	11	27%	$250
Contractor/Per Diem	16	$45.00	7	0%	—
Self-Employed	13	$65.00	2	0%	—
Other	25	—	1	0%	—

Note: — = insufficient data for tabulation.

Table 14.5. Part-Time Hourly Compensation, OTAs: Mental Health Setting

	Median Hours Worked	Median Hourly Rate	Number of Respondents	Receiving Additional Cash Compensation	Median Additional Cash Compensation
Total	**20**	**$20.00**	**7**	**14%**	**$1,000**
Hourly Part-Time	20	$20.00	5	20%	$1,000
Contractor/Per Diem	18	$17.50	2	0%	—

Note: — = insufficient data for tabulation.

Table 14.6. Benefits Received: Mental Health Setting

	OT Full-Time	OT Part-Time	OTA Full-Time	OTA Part-Time
Sample Size	**206**	**21**	**23**	**7**
Health Insurance	90.8%	40.0%	95.7%	14.3%
Dental Insurance	84.0%	44.0%	87.0%	14.3%
Life Insurance	70.9%	28.0%	87.0%	28.6%
Professional Liability Insurance	39.3%	24.0%	43.5%	28.6%
Disability Insurance (Short- or Long-Term)	64.6%	28.0%	56.5%	28.6%
State Licensure	7.8%	0.0%	8.7%	0.0%
AOTA Member Dues	4.9%	0.0%	8.7%	0.0%
Continuing Education	55.3%	20.0%	56.5%	28.6%
College Tuition or Advanced Practice Certification	22.3%	0.0%	13.0%	0.0%
Paid Time Off (Vacation or Sick Leave)	95.1%	52.0%	100.0%	28.6%
Company-Paid Traditional Pension Plan	44.2%	24.0%	30.4%	14.3%
Employee-Funded Retirement Plan (e.g., 401K)	70.4%	40.0%	69.6%	14.3%

Module 15.
Setting Focus: Schools

Table 15.1. Demographic Snapshot: Schools Setting

		Schools Setting	Full Sample
	Total Sample Size	**2,238**	**11,779**
	Median Age, Years	**42**	**39**
Gender	Female	94.8%	90.9%
	Male	4.8%	8.8%
OT/OTA Status	OT	85.8%	82.0%
	OTA	14.2%	18.0%
Highest Degree Held in Occupational Therapy	Certificate	1.1%	1.0%
	Associate's Degree	13.3%	16.8%
	Baccalaureate Degree	30.7%	26.6%
	Master's Degree	50.0%	49.4%
	Professional Doctorate Degree	3.1%	3.9%
	PhD	0.2%	0.9%
	ScD	0.0%	0.1%
	Other	1.7%	1.4%
Hold Advanced Certification/ Recognition	Currently Hold	17.1%	18.6%
	Pursuing	3.0%	5.2%
	Plan to Start	13.8%	18.2%
	No Plans to Start	66.1%	58.0%
Ethnic Background	African-American/Black	2.7%	3.1%
	American Indian/Alaskan Native	0.3%	0.3%
	Asian/Pacific Islander	2.8%	4.4%
	Caucasian/White	87.8%	85.3%
	Hispanic/Latino	2.8%	3.2%
	Multiethnic	1.6%	1.4%
	Prefer Not to Respond	2.1%	2.2%

(Continued)

Table 15.1. Demographic Snapshot: Schools Setting *(cont.)*

		Schools Setting	Full Sample
Total Years of Experience (Median)	Professional	13	9
	In Current Position at Current Setting	7	4
Region	Northeast	30.8%	22.0%
	South Atlantic	18.3%	17.0%
	South Central	7.4%	12.9%
	North Central	24.4%	29.0%
	Mountain	7.6%	7.3%
	Pacific	11.5%	11.9%
AOTA Membership Status	Member	58.2%	58.6%
	Former Member	37.5%	37.2%
	Nonmember	4.3%	4.2%

Note: Percentages do not add to 100 due to rounding as well as "Other" and "Prefer not to answer" responses.

Table 15.2. Annual Compensation, Full-Time OTs: Schools Setting

		Number of Responses	Median Compensation	Receiving Additional Cash Compensation	Median Additional Cash Received
	Overall	**1,605**	**$61,600**	**30%**	**$1,000**
Years of Professional Experience	0–5	447	$53,000	29%	$1,000
	5.1–10	226	$60,000	31%	$1,200
	10.1–15	248	$60,000	27%	$1,000
	15.1–25	356	$67,000	32%	$1,100
	25+	328	$71,000	29%	$1,500
Years in Current Position at Present Setting	0–2	286	$54,000	23%	$1,000
	2.1–5	450	$59,000	33%	$1,000
	5.1–10	249	$63,000	22%	$1,600
	10+	620	$68,000	33%	$1,200
Highest Degree Held in Occupational Therapy	Associate's Degree	1	$78,000	0%	—
	Baccalaureate Degree	553	$64,000	28%	$1,000
	Master's Degree	952	$60,000	30%	$1,000
	Professional Doctorate Degree	65	$74,000	32%	$2,000
	Other	34	$65,500	29%	$1,000
Advanced Practice Certification/Recognition	Hold	301	$60,000	32%	$1,200
	Do Not Presently Hold	1,304	$71,000	29%	$,1000

(Continued)

Table 15.2. Annual Compensation, Full-Time OTs: Schools Setting *(cont.)*

		Number of Responses	Median Compensation	Receiving Additional Cash Compensation	Median Additional Cash Received
Region	Northeast	491	$65,000	30%	$1,000
	South Atlantic	312	$58,000	29%	$1,000
	South Central	120	$61,000	21%	$2,000
	North Central	380	$58,000	31%	$1,000
	Mountain	108	$57,310	30%	$1,100
	Pacific	194	$69,000	34%	$1,350
Setting Location	Urban	544	$63,000	32%	$1,000
	Suburban	762	$63,000	30%	$1,000
	Rural	299	$56,000	26%	$1,000
Control/Ownership	Government	1,163	$62,000	28%	$1,200
	Private For Profit	128	$65,000	39%	$1,000
	Private Nonprofit	168	$60,000	41%	$1,000
	Other	74	$65,000	26%	$1,200
	Unsure	72	$56,500	18%	$750
Employment Status	Employee	1,448	$61,500	31%	$1,000
	Contractor/Per Diem	119	$61,500	19%	$1,000
	Self-Employed	38	$65,000	24%	$1,800

Note: Data are for respondents working 30 or more hours per week. — = insufficient data for tabulation.

Table 15.3. Annual Compensation, Full-Time OTAs: Schools Setting

		Number of Responses	Median Compensation	Receiving Additional Cash Compensation	Median Additional Cash Received
	Overall	**242**	**$36,000**	**25%**	**$515**
Years of Professional Experience	0–5	84	$34,000	23%	$500
	5.1–10	51	$34,500	22%	$500
	10.1–15	29	$38,750	24%	$1,000
	15.1–25	57	$41,000	30%	$515
	25+	21	$39,000	33%	$1,334
Years in Current Position at Present Setting	0–2	42	$33,250	19%	$434
	2.1–5	72	$35,000	28%	$500
	5.1–10	45	$37,643	24%	$600
	10+	83	$40,000	27%	$650

(Continued)

Table 15.3. Annual Compensation, Full-Time OTAs: Schools Setting *(cont.)*

		Number of Responses	Median Compensation	Receiving Additional Cash Compensation	Median Additional Cash Received
Highest Degree Held in Occupational Therapy	Associate's Degree	223	$36,000	25%	$500
	Baccalaureate Degree	5	$44,000	40%	—
	Master's Degree	1	—	0%	—
	Professional Doctorate Degree	0	—	0%	—
	Other	13	$37,000	31%	$1,000
Advanced Practice Certification/Recognition	Hold	5	$46,500	60%	$500
	Do Not Presently Hold	237	$36,000	24%	$558
Region	Northeast	65	$38,000	31%	$600
	South Atlantic	37	$40,000	24%	$1,000
	South Central	18	$43,900	33%	$500
	North Central	85	$33,000	19%	$500
	Mountain	17	$42,000	35%	$2,250
	Pacific	20	$40,500	20%	$684
Setting Location	Urban	66	$35,000	27%	$600
	Suburban	104	$37,750	18%	$500
	Rural	72	$35,700	33%	$750
Control/Ownership	Government	150	$36,000	24%	$600
	Private For Profit	26	$39,000	46%	$500
	Private Nonprofit	25	$40,000	24%	$650
	Other	13	$30,000	23%	$500
	Unsure	28	$34,000	14%	$2,050
Employment Status	Employee	215	$36,000	26%	$500
	Contractor/Per Diem	24	$40,000	21%	$2,000
	Self-Employed	3	$50,000	33%	—

Note: Data are for respondents working 30 or more hours per week. — = insufficient data for tabulation.

Table 15.4. Part-Time Hourly Compensation, OTs: Schools Setting

	Median Hours Worked	Median Hourly Rate	Number of Respondents	Receiving Additional Cash Compensation	Median Additional Cash Compensation
Total	**20**	**$52.00**	**202**	**10%**	**$800**
Hourly Part-Time	20	$46.00	66	20%	$400
Contractor/Per Diem	19	$55.00	107	5%	$9,000
Self-Employed	16	$68.00	25	4%	$1,800
Other	24	$47.00	4	25%	$1,000

Note: — = insufficient data for tabulation.

Table 15.5. Part-Time Hourly Compensation, OTAs: Schools Setting

	Median Hours Worked	Median Hourly Rate	Number of Respondents	Receiving Additional Cash Compensation	Median Additional Cash Compensation
Total	**22.0**	**$27.00**	**65**	**14%**	**$300**
Hourly Part-Time	20.5	$25.00	34	21%	$330
Contractor/Per Diem	23.0	$28.00	28	7%	$175
Self-Employed	25.0	—	2	0%	—
Other	8.0	—	1	0%	—

Note: — = insufficient data for tabulation.

Table 15.6. Benefits Received: Schools Setting

	OT Full-Time	OT Part-Time	OTA Full-Time	OTA Part-Time
Sample Size	**1,605**	**202**	**242**	**65**
Health Insurance	79.4%	23.8%	68.2%	19.7%
Dental Insurance	73.1%	22.2%	64.5%	13.2%
Life Insurance	58.1%	19.7%	51.2%	11.8%
Professional Liability Insurance	32.0%	14.0%	27.3%	13.2%
Disability Insurance (Short- or Long-Term)	44.4%	15.6%	40.5%	3.9%
State Licensure	13.5%	4.4%	16.5%	7.9%
AOTA Member Dues	7.8%	4.4%	7.9%	0.0%
Continuing Education	59.0%	32.1%	55.8%	31.6%
College Tuition or Advanced Practice Certification	10.2%	5.7%	7.4%	5.3%
Paid Time Off (Vacation or Sick Leave)	80.9%	37.5%	81.0%	36.8%
Company-Paid Traditional Pension Plan	43.5%	18.1%	33.9%	11.8%
Employee-Funded Retirement Plan (e.g., 401K)	48.5%	23.5%	48.3%	18.4%

Module 16
Setting Focus: Other Settings

Table 16.1. Demographic Snapshot: Other Settings

		Other Setting	Full Sample
	Total Sample Size	**182**	**11,779**
	Median Age, Years	**46.5**	**39**
Gender	Female	83.5%	90.9%
	Male	15.9%	8.8%
OT/OTA Status	OT	90.1%	82.0%
	OTA	9.9%	18.0%
Highest Degree Held in Occupational Therapy	Certificate	0.0%	1.0%
	Associate's Degree	9.9%	16.8%
	Baccalaureate Degree	37.4%	26.6%
	Master's Degree	44.5%	49.4%
	Professional Doctorate Degree	5.0%	3.9%
	PhD	1.1%	0.9%
	ScD	0.6%	0.1%
	Other	1.7%	1.4%
Hold Advanced Certification/ Recognition	Currently Hold	31.2%	18.6%
	Pursuing	5.5%	5.2%
	Plan to Start	14.8%	18.2%
	No Plans to Start	48.4%	58.0%
Ethnic Background	African-American/Black	1.7%	3.1%
	American Indian/Alaskan Native	0.0%	0.3%
	Asian/Pacific Islander	3.3%	4.4%
	Caucasian/White	88.5%	85.3%
	Hispanic/Latino	2.8%	3.2%
	Multiethnic	2.2%	1.4%
	Prefer Not to Respond	1.7%	2.2%

(Continued)

Table 16.1. Demographic Snapshot: Other Settings *(cont.)*

		Other Setting	Full Sample
Total Years of Experience (Median)	Professional	15	9
	In Current Position at Current Setting	5	4
Region	Northeast	14.3%	22.0%
	South Atlantic	19.2%	17.0%
	South Central	12.1%	12.9%
	North Central	31.9%	29.0%
	Mountain	8.2%	7.4%
	Pacific	14.3%	11.9%
AOTA Membership Status	Member	67.6%	58.6%
	Former Member	29.7%	37.2%
	Nonmember	2.8%	4.2%

Note: Percentages do not add to 100 due to rounding as well as "Other" and "Prefer not to answer" responses.

Table 16.2. Annual Compensation, Full-Time OTs: Other Settings

		Number of Responses	Median Compensation	Receiving Additional Cash Compensation	Median Additional Cash Received
	Overall	**134**	**$71,000**	**29%**	**$1,000**
Years of Professional Experience	0–5	34	$64,300	21%	$700
	5.1–10	21	$70,000	48%	$750
	10.1–15	16	$69,500	38%	$3,000
	15.1–25	26	$70,000	27%	$500
	25+	37	$82,000	24%	$5,000
Years in Current Position at Present Setting	0–2	30	$64,300	7%	—
	2.1–5	44	$70,000	41%	$750
	5.1–10	22	$72,750	41%	$500
	10+	38	$81,000	26%	$4,900
Highest Degree Held in Occupational Therapy	Associate's Degree	0	—	0%	—
	Baccalaureate Degree	52	$78,500	23%	$3,900
	Master's Degree	68	$68,000	34%	$700
	Professional Doctorate Degree	11	$79,000	27%	$500
	Other	3	$121,000	33%	—
Advanced Practice Certification/Recognition	Hold	43	$70,000	35%	$800
	Do Not Presently Hold	91	$73,000	26%	$1,000

(Continued)

Table 16.2. Annual Compensation, Full-Time OTs: Other Settings (cont.)

		Number of Responses	Median Compensation	Receiving Additional Cash Compensation	Median Additional Cash Received
Region	Northeast	21	$67,000	29%	$1,500
	South Atlantic	26	$81,000	31%	$450
	South Central	15	$68,000	27%	$1,300
	North Central	39	$70,000	31%	$550
	Mountain	12	$76,500	33%	$3,000
	Pacific	21	$85,000	24%	$4,000
Setting Location	Urban	72	$71,500	26%	$1,500
	Suburban	41	$70,000	41%	$500
	Rural	21	$73,000	14%	$100
Control/Ownership	Government	39	$72,000	15%	$750
	Private For Profit	60	$73,000	37%	$2,500
	Private Nonprofit	30	$70,000	30%	$700
	Other	2	$69,803	50%	—
	Unsure	3	$55,000	33%	—
Employment Status	Employee	117	$70,000	28%	$1,000
	Contractor/Per Diem	6	$85,000	33%	—
	Self-Employed	11	$116,500	36%	$8,500

Note: Data are for respondents working 30 or more hours per week. — = insufficient data for tabulation.

Table 16.3. Annual Compensation, Full-Time OTAs: Other Settings

		Number of Responses	Median Compensation	Receiving Additional Cash Compensation	Median Additional Cash Received
	Overall	**14**	**$38,500**	**29%**	**$900**
Years of Professional Experience	0–5	9	$37,000	11%	—
	5.1–10	0	—	0%	—
	10.1–15	1	—	0%	—
	15.1–25	2	—	50%	—
	25+	2	—	100%	—
Years in Current Position at Present Setting	0–2	5	$28,500	20%	—
	2.1–5	0	—	0%	—
	5.1–10	7	$45,000	0%	—
	10+	2	—	100%	—

(Continued)

Table 16.3. Annual Compensation, Full-Time OTAs: Other Settings (cont.)

		Number of Responses	Median Compensation	Receiving Additional Cash Compensation	Median Additional Cash Received
Highest Degree Held in Occupational Therapy	Associate's Degree	14	$38,500	29%	$900
	Baccalaureate Degree	—	—	0%	—
	Master's Degree	—	—	0%	—
	Professional Doctorate Degree	—	—	0%	—
	Other	—	—	0%	—
Advanced Practice Certification/Recognition	Hold	1	—	100%	—
	Do Not Presently Hold	13	$39,000	23%	$1,000
Region	Northeast	1	—	0%	—
	South Atlantic	2	—	50%	—
	South Central	3	$45,000	33%	—
	North Central	6	$36,500	33%	—
	Mountain	0	—	0%	—
	Pacific	2	—	0%	—
Setting Location	Urban	5	$40,000	40%	—
	Suburban	6	$44,000	33%	—
	Rural	3	$38,000	0%	—
Control/Ownership	Government	3	$38,000	33%	—
	Private For Profit	8	$38,500	25%	—
	Private Nonprofit	2	$47,000	0%	—
	Other	1	—	0%	—
	Unsure	0	—	0%	—
Employment Status	Employee	13	$39,000	31%	$1,000
	Contractor/Per Diem	1	—	0%	—
	Self-Employed	0	—	0%	—

Note: Data are for respondents working 30 or more hours per week. — = insufficient data for tabulation.

Table 16.4. Part-Time Hourly Compensation, OTs: Other Settings

	Median Hours Worked	Median Hourly Rate	Number of Respondents	Receiving Additional Cash Compensation	Median Additional Cash Compensation
Total	**20.0**	**$45.00**	**27**	**30%**	**$500**
Hourly Part-Time	20.0	$37.00	8	38%	$500
Contractor/Per Diem	20.0	$50.00	10	20%	$175
Self-Employed	22.5	$122.50	8	25%	$8,500
Other	21.0	—	1	0%	$500

Note: — = insufficient data for tabulation.

Table 16.5. Part-Time Hourly Compensation, OTAs: Other Settings

	Median Hours Worked	Median Hourly Rate	Number of Respondents	Receiving Additional Cash Compensation	Median Additional Cash Compensation
Total	**16.5**	**$25.00**	**4**	**0%**	**—**
Hourly Part-Time	20.0	—	1	0%	—
Contractor/Per Diem	13.0	$30.00	3	0%	—

Note: — = insufficient data for tabulation.

Table 16.6. Benefits Received: Other Settings

	OT Full-Time	OT Part-Time	OTA Full-Time	OTA Part-Time
Sample Size	**134**	**27**	**14**	**4**
Health Insurance	75.4%	10.0%	42.9%	—
Dental Insurance	64.9%	3.3%	35.7%	—
Life Insurance	54.5%	10.0%	50.0%	—
Professional Liability Insurance	49.3%	33.3%	50.0%	—
Disability Insurance (Short- or Long-Term)	58.2%	6.7%	42.9%	—
State Licensure	26.1%	20.0%	28.6%	—
AOTA Member Dues	29.1%	20.0%	7.1%	—
Continuing Education	63.4%	36.7%	57.1%	—
College Tuition or Advanced Practice Certification	11.9%	0.0%	7.1%	—
Paid Time Off (Vacation or Sick Leave)	85.1%	20.0%	71.4%	—
Company-Paid Traditional Pension Plan	24.6%	6.7%	35.7%	—
Employee-Funded Retirement Plan (e.g., 401K)	64.2%	33.3%	50.0%	—

Note: — = insufficient data for tabulation.